D1217786

M. Z. THOMAS

Alexander von Humboldt

Scientist, Explorer, Adventurer

ILLUSTRATED BY ULRIK SCHRAMM

TRANSLATED BY ELIZABETH BROMMER

PANTHEON BOOKS

Original edition: *Draussen Wartet das Abenteuer*
Franz Schneider Verlag, München, Germany

Copyright © 1960, by Pantheon Books Inc.
333 Sixth Avenue, New York 14, N.Y.
Library of Congress Catalog Number: 60–7028
Manufactured in the U. S. A.

CONTENTS

ALEXANDER VON HUMBOLDT

Adventure Beckons

THE boy who squatted on the sandy shore of the lake was ten years old. His tousled hair hung down from his forehead, and his two hands looked like the paws of a little dog busy digging itself a lair. He examined carefully the pebbles washed up by the waves, and selected only the best. A few years earlier he could have shown the stones to his father, who had understood so well why one wanted to take home pebbles or plants, butterflies or salamanders, and who had known their right names and where they came from. But his father had died and now no one besides himself was interested in such things.

For whole evenings the boy had sat listening with burning ears to his father's stories about how Columbus discovered the New World, how the brave Spaniard Vasco Núñez de Balboa set off with his clever dog Leoncillo for the South Seas, or how Captain Cook went all around the world for the first time. When the stories were finished his father would tell him to close his wide-open mouth and then they would both laugh.

The boy sighed. There are still so many questions I should have liked to ask him, he thought.

Suddenly, a branch broke in the willow bushes behind him. He jumped up but had no time to hide in the tall reeds before Herr Kunth, his tutor, bore down on him from the edge of the slope, his eyes gleaming with rage and the tails of his frock coat fluttering in the wind.

He seized the boy roughly. "So here you are. There was I, shouting myself hoarse in the park, and you didn't think it necessary to answer me. What are you doing?"

The boy raised his head and his blue eyes looked astonished. "I have been collecting stones," he said in a low voice.

The tutor's face turned purple. "So! You collect stones instead of attending lessons. When you are asked to recite a

poem you are struck dumb, you can't do your sums, Latin is beyond you, and even at German you are so bad one might doubt if it is your native language. But collecting stones and playing at Robinson Crusoe you are good at. Give me those stones at once."

The boy rummaged about in his pockets. It was a long time before he produced a handful of pebbles. There were lovely pink ones and snow-white ones, some edged with silver, and others with green or chestnut-brown rims. The tutor threw them in a wide arc into the lake.

"Pebbles indeed!" A resounding slap landed on the boy's cheek. "I'll teach you to miss your lessons." The next blow struck the forehead and the eye. "We'll go to see your mother at once."

Silently, they climbed up the slope. In the park surrounding the big house the nightingales were singing at midday as if to console the boy. Though he could hear their song, he could not see them very well because there was a tear in his eye. Not that he was crying, the tear was there only because the second blow had gone right into his eye.

The old house basked dreamily in the sun. The boy opened the gate and was just about to slip through when he remembered his manners and let Herr Kunth pass ahead of him.

In the dark hall he quickly brushed the back of his hand over his eyes while Herr Kunth knocked loudly on Frau von Humboldt's door.

She was sitting as usual in the window, and on the sofa lay the old setter Belcastel. "What is it?" she asked.

"Alexander has cut his lessons again. I found him playing about by the lake, collecting pebbles."

Distressed, she turned to the boy. "Pebbles? But you are too big for that. What would your father say? I hear nothing but complaints about you from all sides. Can't you see that you will come to a bad end this way?"

She paused to allow her son to say he was sorry, but he remained silent. He listened to the nightingales trilling away outside. One of them sat on a branch of the oak tree his father had planted close to the window.

"Look at your hands!" exclaimed Frau von Humboldt. Alexander quickly hid them behind his back. "Aren't you ashamed to run about with your hands in such a state? What will become of you?"

Alexander had often asked himself the same question, but he had not yet found a good answer.

At this moment his brother Bill shot into the room. "The King is here!" he shouted, and turning on his heels he disappeared again as quickly as he had come. Before the door clicked to, Alexander had slipped out as well. "You can't go with those hands," his mother called after him, but it was too late.

"He is incorrigible." Herr Kunth croaked, shaking with indignation. "He will bring shame on the family name. All his forebears distinguished themselves in the service of their country, but for him I fear the worst."

"I can't understand it," replied Alexander's mother in her

gentle voice. "He doesn't seem to be able to learn anything."

"I shall do all I can to remind him of his duties and obligations," Herr Kunth assured her.

The boy about whom the two grownups were so concerned chased after his brother William. "Thanks for getting me out of this," he panted while running.

"Had to be done, Kies." The nickname came from the German word for pebbles, *Kieselsteine,* which Alexander was so fond of collecting.

Breathless, they reached the street as an old man, accompanied by three officers, came slowly riding by. He wore a three-cornered hat, and his small body was crippled by gout. A stick with a crook dangled by a loop from his right wrist.

The two boys made deep bows. The rider, in a worn and stained blue uniform, led his horse toward the boys. At the same time he pulled a snuffbox out of his pocket and took a pinch. Tobacco flakes spilled all over his coat. Kies, who had been polishing his hands on his trouser seat, became more confident at the sight of this coat.

The rider stopped in front of Bill and, fixing his steely blue eyes on him, asked, "What is your name?"

"Wilhelm von Humboldt, Your Majesty."

"Why aren't you in the military academy? Don't you want to be a soldier?"

"No, Your Majesty. I would rather be a student."

"Hm." The blue eyes switched to Kies. "And you, young man?"

"Alexander von Humboldt, Your Majesty."

"Alexander? That was the name of a great hero who conquered the world. Do you want to conquer the world too?"

Kies looked straight at the King, and then his eye caught sight of the sword hanging from the saddle. Smiling mischievously he answered, "Yes, Your Majesty, but not with the sword."

At that the King burst into loud laughter, took another pinch of snuff, and rode off still laughing.

The two boys watched him go. "Did you think that's what a king would be like?" asked Bill.

"Not just any king, but I had imagined Frederick the Great exactly like this." Kies' voice was full of admiration, but what had made the greatest impression on him was the stained blue coat the Prussian King had worn.

A green beetle hurried across the street and Kies bent down to pick it up and examine it. "Ah—I've got three of those already," he said and let it go.

Throughout his boyhood Kies remained what Herr Kunth sometimes called a hopeless case and sometimes a blockhead. Kies knew all the birds and butterflies, beetles and trees in the park of his home, but not a single irregular Latin verb. He could remember every stone on the shore of the lake which he continued to explore, but not one mathematical formula. For hours he would gaze with rapt attention at pictures of the Ganges or some other far-off place, but one look at his French grammar gave him a headache.

He was a ceaseless worry to his mother and the despair of his teachers. Every year he lay in bed for weeks on end with one illness after another, and he felt quite sorry for the grown-ups around him to whom he was a continuous anxiety.

On the other hand, he found his illnesses very convenient. Then Herr Kunth could make no objection when he read adventure and travel books. He devoured the accounts of naturalists and explorers who had been the first to penetrate into unknown lands. When he had finished a book, he lay for hours with his eyes wide open, wanting to know the answers to a thousand questions. But no one could tell him what a jungle really looked like, how brightly the stars in the Southern Cross shone in the sky when it guided the Cape Horn navigators, how big the South Seas were, or how high the flames of the erupting volcano were on Tenerife.

All living things interested him, and his curiosity grew with each book he read. "I want to become a naturalist," he said to his mother. She stroked his tousled hair and reminded him to go and have it cut.

"I mean it," he assured her solemnly.

She smiled. "All our family have always been civil servants or soldiers. Forget about these wild notions."

He did not contradict her. It would have been ungrateful and unkind to rebel against her and, besides, he knew it wouldn't be any use. So he kept silent but began to look around for some new activity. His mother suggested that he might like to learn drawing. "You have a gift for it and I shall be glad to pay for your lessons."

This seemed not at all a bad idea. Alexander took some of his sketches to a painter and engraver called Chodowiecki and asked if he would give him drawing lessons. Chodowiecki looked at his sketches and agreed. Alexander was then fifteen.

When he started drawing plants from nature he realized with alarm how few of them he knew by their names. The different kinds of ferns and moss that he learned to draw very carefully and accurately were totally unknown to him.

This ignorance, of which he had never been aware, annoyed him, and from then on he spent his spare time with a young botanist who taught him how to classify plants and assemble a herbarium. He found that to do this he needed to know Latin, for the scientific names of all plants were in Latin and only by using those names could the different spe-

15

cies be distinguished beyond question. Latin for him was now not quite as dead and dry as he had always thought. There was some point in memorizing lists of Latin words after all. What was more, he discovered to his astonishment that the ancient Romans had borrowed many words from the Greeks and that it was a help to know Greek as well. Gradually he became familiar with both these languages.

As his thirst for knowledge grew, he ceased to be satisfied with knowing merely the name and appearance of a plant. He wanted to know where it grew and why it liked a particular soil and situation. This led him by slow degrees to geology and to mineralogy, where he met again his old friends, the pebbles from the lake near his home. And as he was also interested in the use man made of different plants, he turned to the study of chemistry and its practical uses in industry.

He did not make it easy for himself. Whatever he was told or read in books he had to examine and prove to himself. It tormented him not to know things, and so he worked hard and painstakingly for years to perfect himself in all the natural sciences.

Herr Kunth now complained that he was working too much. The blockhead of earlier days was now better informed in some subjects than his tutor.

One day Alexander said to his mother, "I want to make a voyage overseas to explore the jungle."

She was horrified. "Do you want me to die of worry while you are out there in the wilderness? Ferdinand Magellan was killed on Mactan in the Philippines, and Captain Cook met his death in Hawaii. Think of all those who have disappeared without a trace! I couldn't bear it."

"But there are dangers everywhere, Mother, even here. And out there in the world there is so much to discover, so much to explore," Alexander pleaded.

"You are attracted by adventure in far-off places, but adventure also means danger." His mother looked directly at him. "Promise me, Alexander, that you won't go. At least not while I am alive. I gave my word to your father on his deathbed that you would learn a regular profession. Being a naturalist is not a profession."

"Oh, Mother!" Alexander protested, but he could see that she was too tired to go on arguing.

"We shall call Herr Kunth. He had your father's complete confidence. He will know what to decide."

Herr Kunth arrived and declared firmly, "Major von Humboldt would never have permitted one of his sons to plunge into useless and dangerous enterprises which could bring neither honors nor fame. You may say what you like, but it is a fact that brave soldiers and faithful government servants receive honors. No one has even thought of honoring a naturalist. Generals occupy the highest positions in the state, and everywhere enjoy the utmost esteem. Has anyone heard the same of a naturalist?"

"All right," interrupted Alexander abruptly. "I shall apply for admittance to the mining academy at Freiberg, and afterward try for a post in the Ministry of Mines." He turned on his heels and left the room with a heavy tread.

Frau von Humboldt sighed with relief. Herr Kunth nodded with a self-satisfied air. Had he not always said that young people needed to be reminded from time to time of their duties and obligations? Once Alexander had become a civil servant his dreams of the South Seas, of snow-covered mountains in the tropics, and of the Southern Cross would be quickly forgotten. Herr Kunth was sure that Alexander would eventually become a quite useful government official.

And so Alexander became a mining expert. At the age of twenty-four, he was named chief surveyor of one of Germany's mining districts.

Meanwhile his brother Bill had married. "Well, Kies, when will you take the plunge?" he asked one day.

"I marry?" Alexander laughed. "What woman would go with me to jungles where no white man has ever set foot?"

"So you are still dreaming of your journey to the tropics?"

Alexander nodded.

"Then all your studies, your practical work . . ."

"They were indispensable!" explained Alexander. "I am grateful to Mother now that she didn't let me go earlier, for the scientific articles that I have had published have made me known to experts in my field."

"What about your position in the civil service?"

"I'm giving that up. I have been offered the management of either the Silesian smelting works or the salt mines in Westphalia. I shall accept neither."

"And what will Mother say?"

"She has nothing to fear, Bill. I have done as she wished and entered an ordinary profession. As I have promised her, I shall never go overseas in her lifetime without her permission."

"And if she doesn't give her permission?"

Alexander smiled. "She has never refused me anything in the long run. But before I ask her again I am going to make a trip to the Alps. I need practice in the use of scientific equipment, and I want to try out some of my new instruments."

"You are a cursedly stubborn fellow, Kies," said Bill, laughing.

So Alexander went to the Alps. He studied the geological stratification of the mountains, got to know his instruments, trained himself on difficult climbs and long walks. At that time he also met many other scientists.

Now at last, after ten years of hard study and preparation, he felt ready to set out on his great venture. He was not sure whether his mother would give him her permission this time. Nor was he ever to know, for Frau von Humboldt suddenly died after a long illness.

Alexander was now free to make his own decisions.

In Search of a Ship

NOVEMBER was gray and it was cold in Berlin on the day when Alexander went to see his botanist friend Willdenow.

"I hear you are now a rich man, since the death of your mother," said the botanist as he removed from a chair a stack of papers on which pressed plants were gummed.

Alexander looked at one of the specimen pages.

"Yes, I shall have quite a bit of money, but if I can persuade you to come with me to South America I'll be happy to spend some of it on our voyage."

Willdenow shook his head. "You know I am collecting in my herbarium the plant life of Berlin and hereabouts. That's a life's work."

"And the plants of tropical jungles don't interest you?"

"I can't leave my work here, Alexander."

It was a definite refusal. To Willdenow, daisies and blades of grass were as important as orchids, and the study of the vegetation of his native city just as exciting as exploring the Amazon.

"I can see that you can't undertake your journey alone, though," he added. "It is much too dangerous. You must find a reliable friend who will not desert you."

Alexander tried another friend who had been a fellow student at the mining academy, but he too refused. "It is quite impossible to get to South America now," he explained. "We should waste our time."

His friend put forward sound arguments against a journey at this particular time. The Spaniards were afraid of rebellion in their South American colonies, and the English fleet was blockading the ports of Europe. In France, Napoleon was arming for war. There was fear and unrest all over the Continent, and every traveler ran the risk of being taken for a spy.

"If everyone had always been so . . . so apprehensive we would still not know about the existence of America," replied Alexander crossly. "The devil take it! I shall go, even if the whole world tries to stop me."

"But for an expedition such as you are planning, you will need many companions; without specialists and assistants you will get nowhere."

Alexander frowned impatiently. "The only thing I need is one reliable person who will share the work with me."

In search of this friend he traveled all over Germany and Austria, and after a whole year he was still alone. In Salzburg he met an Englishman, a Lord Bristol, who invited Alexander to sail from Italy to Egypt with him in his yacht. Alexander accepted the invitation enthusiastically. Till then he had taken no special interest in Egypt, but now he eagerly prepared himself for the coming trip to the Nile valley. He went to Paris to study archaeology in the museums and libraries there.

As luck would have it, however, Napoleon chose this precise moment to invade Egypt and challenge Britain's supremacy on the high seas. The French fleet sailed out of Toulon with an army of thirty-five thousand men. And Lord Bristol was arrested by the French authorities in Milan.

Alexander saw his hopes of a voyage to Egypt shattered.

He approached French naturalists who knew of him through the articles he had had published, and was received by them with true Parisian hospitality. When he spoke of his plans to go overseas, they told him that the French government was equipping an expedition for a journey around the world. Immediately Alexander determined to join it. In order to become better known in French scientific circles, he gave a course of lectures at the Paris National Institute on the chemical constitution of the atmosphere.

But once again Napoleon interfered with his plans. Needing every penny he could lay hands on for his armies, Napoleon confiscated the money set aside for the expedition. True, it was said that the undertaking had only been indefinitely postponed, but Alexander knew enough about the ways of the world not to be taken in by this.

He made his way to his hotel in the Saint-Germain district of Paris, in the Rue du Vieux-Colombier—the street of the pigeonhouse—which took its name from a dovecot where the monks of the abbey of Saint-Germain-des-Prés once upon a time bred pigeons for their modest Sunday dinners. This was the students' quarter and near by was the district known as La Charité, where idealists dreamed their daring dreams of freedom.

Freedom indeed! thought Alexander bitterly. With what optimism and enthusiasm he had dreamed of his great expedition! Now fate seemed determined to stop him at every turn. What a simpleton he had been to come to Paris in the first place. He was wasting his money, buying books and instruments and studying Egyptology instead of doing a useful job at home as a civil servant. For more than a year now he had wandered from town to town, and all his efforts had got him exactly nowhere.

Stepping out briskly, he reached his hotel as dusk fell over the steeply slanting roofs. Impatiently he tore open the door. In the dim hall he bumped into a young man and murmured an apology. The porter handed him his key and a candle. As Alexander turned to the staircase he saw by the flickering light of the candle that the young man carried a battered botanical specimen box on a string slung over his shoulder.

Surprised, Alexander stopped and asked, "Are you a botanist?"

The young man smiled. He was poorly dressed and seemed to be one of the many students of Paris.

"My name is Bonpland," he replied politely, "by profession a medical man." Then he added, with a touch of irony, "But I would advise you to consult another doctor should you ever need one."

While he spoke he looked searchingly at Alexander, who wore the dark blue frock coat in fashion at the time, a snow-white cravat, a yellow waistcoat, striped knee breeches, and tight-fitting boots, their tops turned down to show the yellow lining, matching the waistcoat.

"A doctor who botanizes!" exclaimed Alexander approvingly, taking no notice of Bonpland's little joke. "Unfortunately few of your colleagues realize how important it is in the practice of medicine to have first-hand knowledge of the healing power of plants."

Bonpland screwed up his nose. "I finished my examinations last year, and the only subject in which I did fairly well was botany. So I devote myself to it more out of gratitude than from medical interest."

Alexander laughed. The young man had a sense of humor. "Ah, so you are more of a botanist than a doctor?"

"If you won't think the worse of me—yes, that is so," agreed Bonpland good-naturedly.

Together the two men climbed the creaking stairs and sat down in Alexander's room. First they both began to talk at the same time, stopped and fell silent, and then they laughed. After that Bonpland told Alexander his life's story.

He had been christened Aimé and was the fourth child of the royal surgeon and leading doctor at the Charité hospital in La Rochelle. He had studied medicine in Paris and been a ship's doctor for a year on a French man-of-war to gain practical experience. After that he took his final examina-

24

tions, but he had much more enthusiasm for flowers and plants than for the infections and carbuncles of his patients. His father expected him to practice medicine in his home town, but Aimé was not at all eager to return to La Rochelle. He did not know exactly what he wanted to do, and so he was all ears when Alexander began to speak of his plans.

Alexander's words conjured up the exciting dreams of every adventure-loving boy. Tropical jungles came to life, flames belched from blazing volcanoes bathed in the red glow of their fire, and emerald-green waterfalls gurgled their secret messages.

All the great explorers and adventurers of the past joined the two men as they sat around the table that night and the following nights, and it all ended—as indeed it had to—by Aimé's shaking his new friend's hand and saying, "Alexander, I'm going with you."

"Now that there are two of us, it will be easier to find a ship to take us to South America," exclaimed Alexander. "Everything is easier for two than for one."

"That's why Don Quixote always had Sancho Panza around," was Aimé's apt reply.

They laughed. They were full of confidence and firmly believed that their dreams of great discoveries would now come true. It seemed to Alexander that fate had only held him back all this time so that he should meet Aimé.

But they still had to find a ship. While all Europe was arming for war, no one thought of providing sea passages for two unknown young men equipped with butterfly net, a botanical specimen box, and sextant. One day, when they were still in Paris, new hope came from Sweden. Alexander rushed to Aimé. "We've got a ship. Get ready at once. We are going to Marseilles. The Swedish Consul will take us on his frigate

25

to Africa, and in Tripoli we'll join a caravan to Mecca. From there we make for India by way of the Persian Gulf."

"Africa? India?" Aimé's brain was in a whirl. "Why have you been learning Spanish then, my friend?"

"How was I to know that we would be going to Asia instead of South America?" Alexander replied impatiently.

Aimé began to pack. "All right then, let us go to the land of the Arabian Nights. There is work for us everywhere."

On October 20, 1798, they left Paris with all their equipment and luggage. They had intended to go on board the frigate at once on reaching Marseilles, but there was no sign of her in the harbor. The Swedish Consul told them he was sure his ship would arrive any day, but weeks went by without a sign of it.

"I always thought the Swedes were reliable people," Aimé grumbled.

"She'll come," said Alexander hopefully, looking at his calendar. It was already the middle of December.

Together they went again to the Swedish Consul and found him in a state of great agitation. "Gentlemen, I have just learned that our ship went down with all hands in a storm off the coast of Portugal."

"What do we do now?" wondered Aimé as they left the Consul's house with long faces.

"We look for another ship in the harbor," decided Alexander.

A few days later, having found a boat preparing to sail for Tunis, they came to terms with the sullen-looking captain about their passage money and took all their provisions on board. All they needed then was the French authorities' permission to leave France. That, however, the harbormaster obstinately refused to give.

"There is rebellion in Tunis," he warned them.

Nothing would change his mind, and at dawn next day the surly captain sailed away without them, but with all their provisions. Bonpland and Alexander stood on the quay fuming with helpless rage.

From the west threatening clouds came racing across the sky and the sea grew choppy. "Who knows," mused Aimé, "if it isn't just as well we didn't sail." Eight days later they knew for certain. The raging sea washed the wreckage of many ships ashore, but their boat and its captain were never seen or heard of again.

"Let's wait a bit longer," suggested Aimé.

"What for?" asked Alexander. "Lord Nelson has destroyed the French fleet off Egypt. In Marseilles we are caught like mice in a trap. Let's try our luck in Spain."

The same week they set out, laden with their equipment, along the Mediterranean coast road to Perpignan and Barcelona. They visited the famous monastery of Montserrat perched among the sheer granite rocks of that mountain and climbed to its summit. Alexander made a survey of the Castilian plain while Aimé collected alpine roses and heather.

Their way led south among palms and locust trees to Valencia and then farther south through olive and orange groves to Murcia, where they turned north in the direction of Madrid across the sun-parched wilderness of La Mancha. They asked for bread at an inn, but there was none to be had and Aimé grumbled, "This is the tenth inn where we couldn't buy bread."

"Come here and hold my compass," interrupted Alexander. "I want to take our bearings. According to my calculations we should cross the thirty-ninth meridian somewhere here."

In a field some distance away an old woman, who was hoeing a row of peas, watched the strangers suspiciously.

"Pedro," she whispered to her husband, who lay in a near-by ditch snoozing, "there are two men over there behaving as though they'd never seen the sun before. They keep staring at it."

Pedro looked up sleepily at the two figures, and then suddenly gaped in open-mouthed astonishment as he saw one of them leap into the air and zigzag across the field. Aimé was chasing a butterfly.

The heat haze distorted their figures, and the old peasant couldn't help bursting into loud laughter at their antics. But the next moment he became silent, and as he scratched his head in bewilderment his face took on a cunning expression. "Do you know who I think they are?" he asked his wife.

She did not.

"Don Quixote and Sancho Panza, that's who they are," the old peasant announced craftily.

"Mother of God, I thought they had been dead a long time."

"Well, just take a look at them," said her husband and laughed.

The mad hopper had returned to his companion, tapping his ridiculous metal box with an air of satisfaction. The other one kept staring through a long expanding tube at the flat countryside, even though there was nothing whatever to see there.

"God's truth!" exclaimed the peasant woman, thrusting her hoe into the dusty ground. "If you think that Don Quixote and Sancho Panza are still alive, it's them all right." And raising her voice she called across the field, "Eh—gentlemen, are you looking for something?"

"We'd like something to eat," answered Alexander.

"And something to drink," added Aimé.

"And you think you will find food and drink by looking through a tube and hopping about like madmen?" she demanded.

"No, my good woman," replied Alexander. "I am taking measurements of the La Mancha plain, and my friend here has caught a butterfly."

"Do you expect to live on butterflies?" inquired the stupefied woman. Her husband handed Alexander the wine bottle, saying, "May it give you strength, sir."

While Alexander drank, the woman whispered to Aimé, "Are you really Sancho Panza?"

At first Aimé looked dumfounded, but then he smiled knowingly. "Oh, so you have recognized us. Yes. Don Quixote and Sancho Panza, that's who we are. We have been away a long time, but at last we have come back and my noble master here now devotes himself to measuring the height of mountains while I pick flowers and trap butterflies and beetles."

"And what do you do it for?" she wanted to know.

"Because we serve a virtuous and demanding lady," replied Aimé.

"Ah, I know, Dulcinea!" exclaimed Pedro with a knowing wink.

Aimé took the wine bottle from Alexander, but before drinking he shook his head and said, "No, she isn't called Dulcinea any more. Her name is Science now."

"But we love her just the same," confirmed Alexander, looking at the wicker basket that stood in the cool shade. The old woman understood his look and gave him two hunks of bread and some goat's cheese.

"And where are you off to now?" asked her husband.

"We are going to the King."

"To the King in Madrid?" The old man thumped his breast with excitement. "What do you want from him?"

"A ship." And with that they went their way.

The old peasant watched them go. "They are even madder than I thought," he said to his wife.

Don Quixote from Berlin and his Sancho Panza from La Rochelle headed for the granite walls of the royal castle in Madrid. "Do you really want to go to see the King?" asked Bonpland. "Remember, you are not a Spanish grandee."

Alexander drew himself up to his full height. "I am a Prussian nobleman, or grandee as you call it. Besides, isn't this the country which gave a poor nobody from Genoa a ship? Aren't we in the land where all great dreams, even those of a Don Quixote, come true?"

"Yes, but we come from Paris, where the King and Queen were quite recently beheaded for the people's amusement. We will be suspected of revolutionary ideas. Their Spanish Majesties will shake with fear when they see us coming."

31

"Let that be *my* worry," replied Alexander in a lordly fashion; and looking at his boots, which were coated with dust from the La Mancha plain, he added, "The most important thing is to get our boots cleaned. After that, I will present myself to His Most Catholic Majesty of Spain and ask for passports to his South American colonies."

On arrival in Madrid, they carted their luggage to an inn by the Manzanares, which Cervantes had called "a brook with the rank and dignity of a river," and had their boots cleaned till they shone.

Next day Alexander shaved with more than usual care and put on the dress uniform of a German mining engineer— plum-colored frock coat with lapels of yellow silk, high starched collar, ornamental epaulettes, and white satin knee breeches. In this attire he presented himself to his country's Ambassador at the Spanish court under his official title of Chief Mine Surveyor Alexander von Humboldt.

The Ambassador received him with the polite, absent-minded air of a busy man who normally exchanged a few pleasant words with his countrymen on a visit to Spain. But Alexander had taken the precaution of finding out about the Ambassador's private hobby, which to his astonishment had turned out to be mineralogy, and he presented him with some choice stones that he had collected in the Pyrenees.

The Ambassador was delighted with this gift and listened with interest to his guest. They talked about rare stones, and Alexander was shown the Ambassador's collection, which he praised highly. After that, what could be more natural than that this distinguished mining expert should be given an introduction to the Spanish Minister for Foreign Affairs!

The Minister greeted Alexander with proverbial Spanish courtesy, but the interview might have resulted in no more than a well-meant handshake if Alexander, again in his uniform, had not at the right moment dropped a remark about his connection with gold, silver, and copper mines. The Minister pricked up his ears and asked Alexander for an account of his experiences in the German mines.

Spain possessed countless mines of precious ore in South America. In Bolivia there were the mercury and copper mines at Potosí; Colombia had the richest gold deposits in the world as well as the famous emerald mines at Muzo; there was copper in Venezuela, gold and silver in Mexico.

The Minister was charmed by Alexander. Here was this pleasant fellow, modestly calling himself a naturalist and yet possessing expert knowledge of mining processes, wanting to undertake a voyage of exploration to South America. Might he not come back with valuable information and important suggestions on more profitable methods of ore extraction? What was more, he might even discover new deposits of precious metals rich enough to be worked. And the best of it was that this strange man insisted on paying the costs of his voyage out of his own pocket on the ground that he wanted to be quite free to carry out his studies as he liked.

The Minister rushed to the royal palace at Aranjuez, where the King, whose coffers were as empty as the bed of the Manzanares was dry, listened to his report with growing interest and gave orders that Alexander should be presented to him at once.

A royal carriage went to fetch Alexander from the inn. The King was astounded at the polished manners of his visitor, who seemed so much at home in the finer points of Spanish court etiquette. Not a word was said about botany or the importance to science of any discoveries that Alexander might make on his voyage.

Instead, the Prussian mining expert revealed his knowledge of politics, which interested the King a great deal more than taking measurements with a sextant to fix the exact location of a particular place.

The King had many worries of his own. There was, for instance, that peculiar General Bonaparte from Corsica, who was said to have his eye on the throne of France. Ah, that general! The Parisian ladies were shocked at first at the way he wore his hair down to his shoulders in what they called "dog's ears." But most people who knew him better had long forgiven him for this, and were now looking to him to end the revolution in France. He had beaten the Mamelukes in sight of the pyramids, and it was unlikely that he would be satisfied with the conquest of Egypt. His army could equally well defeat the Jacobin radicals in Paris. Nothing made pleasanter hearing to a king than the news that the guillotine—that invention by a French doctor which had caused the absolute monarchs of Europe many anxious moments in recent years—might be abolished.

The audience was a great success. The visitor told amusing stories to enliven the serious conversation. He was showered with so many royal favors that when he returned to Madrid his head was in a whirl. He had won the decisive battle of his life.

Back at the inn, he shouted, "Aimé, we are going to South America under the special protection of the Spanish crown. We can collect what we like and as much as we like—animals, plants, stones. Each of us is going to be issued a permit giving us a completely free hand."

"What, me too?"

"Yes, you too, my friend. You will have the right to botanize to your heart's content even without me, in case you get tired of me. We will receive letters to the Spanish authorities overseas, instructing them to help us in our work. Every Spanish ship will be requested to take us aboard."

Aimé could hardly speak. "But . . . but such privileges have never been given to foreigners before."

"Be satisfied that they have been given to us."

"How ever did you manage it?"

"To tell you the truth, Aimé, I think your confidence in me gave me the courage to do what I did and win Spain to our cause. You were the first person who ever really believed in me."

"I shall begin to learn Spanish this very minute," declared Aimé enthusiastically.

Farewell to Europe

ALL units of the British navy had been ordered to stop Spanish ships from leaving port or entering a Spanish harbor in either Spain itself or her American colonies. The whole Atlantic coast was blockaded and every Spaniard on the high seas risked being sunk or captured.

The guns of an English man-of-war and several frigates pointed menacingly at the narrow channel that connected the harbor of La Coruña with the open sea. Here, in Spain's most important Atlantic port, lay the corvette *Pizarro* safely at anchor. Thanks to chance and the audacity of her captain, she had completed the long journey from Rio without mishap, but now she rolled idly in harbor, stealing, as it were, an occasional furtive glance at the English forces waiting outside for the opportunity to put a broadside into her.

The captain of the *Pizarro* was whistling a tune to himself. He was quite glad of the enforced rest. There were pretty girls in La Coruña and he had enough rum on board to while away the time.

A boat with three landlubbers, all dressed as if they were going to a ball, was heading toward him. One of them, the harbormaster Don Clavigo, the captain already knew.

"Buenos días, Señores," he greeted them.

"Captain, is your ship ready to sail?" asked the harbormaster without preliminaries. "His Majesty the King wants you to take these two gentlemen to South America."

"With the greatest of pleasure," answered the captain. "But please be good enough to convey the royal wish also to the captain of the British battleship over there."

The harbormaster leaned forward and lowered his voice. "It is a command, Captain. On the way you are to drop anchor at Tenerife and stay there as long as the gentlemen wish it. At sea, they are to be allowed to make whatever observations they desire."

The captain eyed the two smartly dressed *caballeros* with amusement. "And what do the gentlemen plan to observe at sea?" he asked.

"They will take temperature readings of the ocean, Captain, and study the changes in temperature at different depths."

The captain looked doubtfully at the harbormaster and scratched himself behind the ear. "The English permitting, I am ready. But tell me," he added with a puzzled frown, "why is it so important to know if the codfish have it warm or cold in their bath? I have never given it a thought in all my life."

"That is why you have not found out that the thermometer can give you warning of sandbanks much earlier than the plumb line. When the temperature on the surface of the water goes down quickly, you are heading for dangerous shallows."

"Is that so, gentlemen? That'd be good news for an old seafarer like me. But you will have to prove it to me. My ship is at your service."

"When can we sail?"

"When the wind blows inland the English have to move farther out to sea to escape being driven against the rocks. Then, with luck, we may be able to hoodwink them."

"And we ourselves, we won't be driven against the cliffs?"

"Ah—that's when you will hang out your thermometer and tell me whenever the water gets colder. Then I shall make a quick turn and we'll be safe."

They all laughed and drank a dram of rum to a safe voyage.

Two days later the barometer was falling. "Now's the time," said the captain. "If you feel like a pleasure cruise, you'd better have your luggage brought aboard quickly."

A storm was blowing up and huge breakers crashed against the rocky coast. Low-lying clouds came racing toward land, and shrieking gulls searched the cliffs for fish washed ashore by the heavy sea.

The harbormaster rushed to the waterfront in his oilskin and signaled, "The English are turning about."

"Set sail," commanded the captain and the heavy tackle creaked into position up the mast. Slowly the *Pizarro* dug her nose into the heaving sea.

A head wind blew straight into the narrow channel, and the English captains never suspected that any ship would be able to slip through the harbor exit in such weather.

It was two o'clock in the afternoon of June 5, 1799.

The captain made a turn to starboard. The *Pizarro* heaved over on her side. "Hard to port!" Smartly the helmsman reversed the tiller, repeating the captain's command, and the *Pizarro* heaved over on the other side. There was hardly enough room for the maneuver, but the turn succeeded.

"Straight ahead!" The rudder turned back and the ship began to straighten slowly. "Steady as you go!" The helmsman tried hard to hold a straight course, but the wind was too strong. The turn to port was lost.

"Slow to starboard! Stop!" The man at the helm threw back the tiller and caught the turn midway. The *Pizarro* veered hard in the raging wind, and the next maneuver succeeded better. The ship fought a brave fight even though she was very nearly dashed against the rocks more than once.

By six o'clock in the evening, they were level with the lighthouse *Hercules,* whose continuously burning coal furnace had been kept alight ever since the days of the Roman emperors. Slowly the *Pizarro* edged past it, and by nine o'clock a faintly flickering light in a fisherman's hut was the last farewell from the continent of Europe.

The storm raged all through the night, but Alexander never tired nor did he feel the least seasick.

"Have you been to sea often, *Señor?*" the captain asked.

"No, never."

"How come you are not seasick, then?"

"Captain, I have been waiting for this moment all my life. For the last fifteen years I have done nothing but prepare myself for it," Alexander explained.

At dawn the topgallant mast broke and seamen had to lower its sail. "This will slow us up by two knots," said the captain, with a curse.

The *Pizarro* was not normally a fast ship, but riding before the strong wind she flew across the water like a wild duck pursued by a bird of prey.

On the evening of the third day the lookout sighted a ship. They had been heading straight into an English convoy. In a flash the helmsman changed course and the *Pizarro* escaped in a westerly direction, saved by approaching nightfall.

No light was allowed to burn on board. Alexander groped around crossly among the hawsers and ropes. How could he take the temperature of the water without a light to read the thermometer by?

The captain could not get over his astonishment at these curious passengers whom the King had wished on him. They behaved like no other passengers he had ever come across in

his long years of seafaring. Instead of hiding themselves in their cabins like most landlubbers, these two spent day and night on deck. It seemed as if they never slept.

They tested the earth's magnetism and measured the speed of the Gulf Stream; they caught jellyfish, electrified them on tin plates, and were delighted to see them light up brightly at a touch.

They hauled up plants from a depth of over fifty fathoms

and discovered a new kind of vinelike alga which had not been known before.

When the *Pizarro* reached the latitude of Gibraltar the wind dropped to a gentle breeze, and she made only very slow progress. The watches were doubled, for now a lighter and faster vessel could overtake her easily. There was uneasiness on board, although Alexander and Aimé were quite unaffected by it. They kept right on filling their notebooks with the results of their experiments, and behaved generally as if there wasn't a single English ship in all the world which would take delight in capturing the *Pizarro* and escorting her back to Lisbon.

A strong current carried the *Pizarro* toward the coast of the volcanic island of Lanzarote in the Canaries one night when the moon stood high above the towering volcanoes. The entire western part of this island had been turned into a wasteland by violent eruptions years earlier, when whole villages were completely destroyed in a single day. Columns of basalt rock rose steeply from the sea to the sky.

Past Lanzarote and the small island of Montaña Clara, famous for its canaries, the *Pizarro* cautiously approached Tenerife, but in the thick fog the captain could not find the harbor entrance and had to drop anchor out at sea. Visibility grew less from minute to minute, and for two hours the ship lay shrouded in a blanket of dense fog. Then suddenly the morning sun pierced the darkness, and the volcano Pico de Teyde rose majestically out of the clouds in brilliant sunlight. Alexander and Aimé rushed to the forecastle.

"Battleship dead astern!" shouted the lookout in the silence.

Close aft lay four British men-of-war, with their sails shortened.

"Raise anchor!" yelled the captain. This was the time when

41

he showed what a sly fox of the sea he really was. Unlike the English, he had left his sails unfurled and the morning breeze now blew into them with full force.

The English were even more surprised than the Spaniards. They had not thought it possible that a ship could sneak past them in the fog. Before their crews could even man the guns, the *Pizarro* had reached the shelter of the fortress of Santa Cruz.

Of this fortress the English had unhappy memories. Here, two years earlier, they had fought a bloody sea battle in which Lord Nelson lost his right arm. Instead of pursuing the *Pizarro* the four battleships withdrew out of reach of the heavy cannons of the fortress.

Aimé was excited and upset by this experience. "The whole world seems in league to stop you from carrying out your peaceful work," he said to Alexander. "You have to consider yourself lucky if you are not shot in the back, and yet all you want is to discover ways and means to make seafaring safer for everybody and to find new plants that will yield healing medicines."

"You must get used to this," answered Alexander philosophically. "Every attempt to do good always meets with bitter opposition. If the bullets of the English don't hit you in Tenerife, it will be the poisoned arrows of Indians later on, or at the end of the voyage the barbed criticisms of your own people at home. They will tell you from their armchairs how much better you ought to have done. But why think about it now in this lovely country?"

Before them, on a small plain, lay the island's capital, surrounded by gardens. White camels came wandering toward them down a hillside covered with laurel, myrrh, and strawberry trees.

This was a Garden of Eden where it was always spring.

Date palms and coconut palms grew on the shore. Higher up were heavily laden bananas, and higher still dragon trees with their serpentlike trunks. The terraced slopes were planted with vines, and dotted about on the hills were groves of cypresses and flowering orange trees which sheltered little chapels. Towering above the whole landscape was the mighty volcano, which showed a new aspect of its imposing height at every step.

Alexander stepped reverently under the immense crown of one of the oldest dragon trees on the island. This majestic old giant was once worshiped as a god. Its trunk had been hollow at the time of Columbus, when monks had said Mass on an altar erected inside it. Alexander and Aimé found that the girth of this huge trunk was more than fifteen yards. They left the tree to turn their attention to the other giant on the island, the volcano itself.

Alexander noted down his impression of the crater and the wonderful view they had when they reached the summit after a long and difficult climb. "We managed to get to the very bottom of the crater, perhaps closer than any naturalist had ever done before. The sulphur fumes burned holes in our clothes, while our fingers turned stiff with frost in a temperature of twelve degrees. In the cracks of the crater the mercury leaped to nearly two hundred degrees, and this at a height of four thousand feet."

Alexander filled a bottle with vapor fumes at the edge of the crater and later tested them for their chemical composition.

He and Aimé were shaking with cold, but when Alexander asked one of the guides for the wine they had brought, the man only laughed and pointed to his Adam's apple. The wine had long ago passed down his own throat!

On the way down, the mild springlike air seemed stiflingly

hot after the biting cold on the summit. Aimé looked for the water bottle, only to find that it, too, had been emptied by the guides while he and Alexander were busily knocking from the crater's edge pieces of porphyritic slate and obsidian rock. They reached the plain half dead from thirst after a nine-hour descent, but these hardships didn't seem to matter much compared with the wonders they had seen.

Voyage under the Southern Cross

AFTER a stay of six days the *Pizarro* raised anchor one stormy June evening and secretly slipped out of the harbor without showing a single light. Her course was the same that Columbus had sailed three hundred years earlier with his three caravels. At that time three Portuguese men-of-war had lain in wait for the Spaniards behind the green promontory of the island; now it was British ships.

But the *Pizarro* reached the open sea without being intercepted. There was no sign of the British as the wind, which had dropped to a gentle breeze, swelled her sails. Great masses of seaweed floated noiselessly by; flying fish leaped out of the water to a height of twenty feet around the bow and hovered in mid-air until an albatross dived among them to pick his prey.

During the following days a haze hid the sky. In his laboratory on deck, Alexander analyzed the vapor fumes from the crater in the test tube of a eudiometer.

He also tested the fins of flying fish for electricity and wrote down his observations about the different kinds of vegetation on Tenerife; thus began the science of plant geography.

Besides, he watched the ever-changing colors of the sea

and sky, carefully grading the varying shades, and he also began to make a systematic study of weather forecasting.

One night, distant lightning flashed through the ragged clouds in the sky. Alexander sat on a coil of rope in the shelter of the bulwark waiting to read the thermometer that he had hung over the side. Suddenly he saw the clouds slowly part amidst the flashes of the electric storm, and there in a silvery glow in the sky appeared the Southern Cross.

He had been waiting for this sight for days, but now it took him by surprise. How often as a small boy had he looked up into the sky with no other wish in his heart than that one day he might be able to see this bright signpost, which had guided all the great navigators of the past!

Three thousand years before the birth of Christ, the inhabitants of Europe could see this constellation of stars every night in their sky, for then it stood ten degrees higher above the southern horizon. When it disappeared from their view forever, the pyramids of Egypt were already five hundred years old.

Alexander had always thought of the Southern Cross as a visible sign and symbol of his hope of freedom, and now, when he saw it shining high above his head, he knew that he had won the long battle of his youth, not only against the prejudice and opposition of other people but also against his own doubts and fears.

Aimé fished the thermometer out of the water and brought it to him, but when he saw the look on Alexander's face he knew at once what had happened.

"I think a lot of people would envy you this moment," he said.

Alexander looked up, surprised. "Envy me—why?"

"Not everyone is lucky enough to find his star," replied his friend.

46

Alexander frowned. "Luck has nothing to do with it," he said. His stubbornness had always made him impatient with vague sentiments of this sort. He contradicted Aimé firmly: "You call it luck that a sickly, stupid boy of whom all his teachers despaired should slave for years to become a scientist, and work and train to make himself strong enough for an expedition into the unknown?"

"That you managed it, that's what I'd call luck," answered Aimé with a grin on his face.

Alexander jumped up impatiently and took the dripping thermometer out of Aimé's hand. "A man can only depend on his own achievements." With this parting shot he walked off and disappeared behind the mast.

Aimé raised his eyebrows. The stars of the Southern Cross seemed to be winking at him from behind a wisp of cloud.

"Well, well, our friend hasn't a good word to say for luck," he mused to the stars; "but for myself I shall take good care not to offend kindly Dame Fortune. Till now I have got along with her famously and I don't object to her giving me a helpful hand now and then."

Hardly were the words out his mouth when a sudden squall struck the ship. Aimé swayed on his feet and clung to the hawsers. At the same time he burst out laughing. "Come on, you mad and lucky wind," he shouted; "show him that knowledge and will power aren't everything. Come and blow us to America!"

When they had crossed the equator, the temperature remained at a steady 99°F. The sun beat down mercilessly until the tar oozed from the joints in the *Pizarro*'s hull and the planks of the deck cracked with the heat. Sweat ran down everyone's face, and some of the steerage passengers, whose quarters were as cramped as a sheep's pen, suffered with fever.

Forward, in the meager shade of the foresail, Alexander was examining various species of sea algae. He was the happiest man on board. He loved the heat after the many cold winters of his North German home, and he would have been whistling a tune but for the old seaman's superstition about whistling on board ship.

Carefully he spread out the fronds of the algae on blotting paper and put them in a press, while noting that there were some species that grew to a tremendous height and that would tower over the tallest trees to be found on land.

The captain came stamping along the deck with a dark face. Aimé was walking beside him, talking excitedly. They stopped when they came to Alexander.

"There is not a single ounce of china bark on board," com-

plained Aimé. "The sick below deck are already delirious. Yesterday we had four cases, today there are nine."

The captain swore in Spanish. "This cursed, hellish heat! We're being roasted alive." He wiped the back of his neck. "Can I help it if the fools get ill?"

"Do you think the situation is serious?" asked Alexander, turning to Aimé.

"Yes!" replied Aimé. "This is an epidemic. One gives it to the other."

"Haven't we got any china bark in our luggage?"

Aimé shook his head. "With all our equipment we never thought of medicines. Besides, I should have thought that a Spanish ship would be well stocked with this bark of Peruvian cinchona trees. It contains quinine and is an invaluable aid against fever."

"Do I run a hospital?" roared the captain. "In my whole life I have never had a fever."

"What does the ship's doctor do for the sick?" asked Alexander.

"Pshaw! He bleeds them and gives them salts," said Aimé contemptuously.

Just then the ship's carpenter came to fetch the captain. A young sailor, nineteen years old and as strong and tough as they come, had collapsed with the fever. He now lay delirious in his bunk. The captain turned abruptly and Aimé followed him.

Alexander bent down again over his plants, which had shriveled in the hot sun. But he hardly looked at them. He was thinking of the sick below deck whose delirious ravings could be heard even on the foredeck.

An epidemic on board! Nothing worse could be imagined. Alexander felt a cold shiver run down his spine. Till now he had always caught every disease that was going, and here

49

on board ship there was no way of escaping it. Was he to succumb to fever before he had even set foot in South America?

He shook himself. If he gave way to such thoughts the battle would be lost before it began. There was nothing more weakening than fear.

To help him to overcome it, he unpacked his instruments and began to take measurements to fix the position of the *Pizarro*.

The helmsman disagreed with his calculations, so Alexander checked them against several reckonings of the moon's position, which he carried out at night, and found them to be correct. But although he now knew where the *Pizarro* was he did not yet know exactly how far from land they were because the French, Spanish, and English sea charts that he compared showed a slightly different coastline for the northern part of South America.

The captain laughed at him. "We have three more days to go before we sight land."

"You are wrong, Captain," contradicted Alexander. "According to my calculations we should sight the coast tomorrow morning at sunrise."

The captain washed down his annoyance at this impertinent remark with a good draught of rum, bit off the end of a cigar, and said, *"Señor,* you must be a great scientist, since the King has given you permission to do whatever you think fit on my ship. But I have sailed this ocean for twenty years and I have always relied on my logbook. You said yourself that you have never been to sea before. If I tell you that we shall see land in three days, you can be sure that it won't be an hour sooner. It would be better if you didn't meddle in affairs that only a seafaring man can understand."

He didn't offer Alexander a cigar or a tot of rum, which was a sure sign that he was very much put out.

Alexander checked and rechecked his figures. They tallied. He compared the charts, taking the mean course where their information varied, and stuck to his assertion.

The captain, purple with rage, stalked off to his cabin.

Next day a strong wind and rain made the sea choppy. From the crow's nest on top of the mast came the full-throated call, "Land in sight!"

Slowly the headland of the island of Tobago rose from the mist on the far horizon. The captain had to look three times through his telescope before he believed his eyes.

"Either you are in league with the devil, *Señor*," he shouted furiously, "or three hundred years of seafaring across this ocean to America has been nothing but a game of chance."

"The devil had nothing to do with my watch and my sextant," said Alexander soothingly. "But I am sure you will agree that we must have accurate calculations and correct charts. In future it will not be good enough to reach one's destination by a hit-or-miss method, leaving the rest to chance. Now we have the means to plot a ship's course accurately and we can have the highest degree of safety at sea."

The captain offered Alexander a cigar, one of his best brand, which he himself smoked only on Sundays. "Please accept my apologies," he said in Spanish. Then he looked him up and down from top to toe and added, "I expect you will get a heap of money and the largest Spanish decoration for your work."

As Alexander laughed and lit his cigar the ship's doctor came along to tell them that during the night several more passengers and seamen had fallen ill.

"We shall make for the nearest port," decided the captain.

"The nearest port is Cumaná," the helmsman informed him. "We can land the sick there the day after tomorrow."

Alexander asked after the young sailor who had collapsed

with the fever on the previous day, and the doctor told him, "He has gone into a decline. I bled him three times, but his fever is as high as ever."

In the evening the calm sea glowed with a fairy-tale shimmer of phosphorescence. Alexander glanced restlessly at the mountainous and rugged coastline illuminated by occasional shafts of moonlight which pierced through the clouds. The only sound to be heard was the monotonous cry of several large sea birds. The *Pizarro* was making only four knots. Would she reach port before the epidemic claimed more victims? wondered Alexander.

He was startled out of his reverie by an eerie, melancholy sound—the toll of the death bell. The young sailor had succumbed to the fever.

The crew knelt where they stood and, crossing themselves, prayed.

Wrapped in a white sail, the body was placed on a makeshift bier and at sunrise the captain ordered the sails to be braced back so that the wind, which now met them in front, brought the *Pizarro* to a standstill. The flag was broken to half-mast, and when a last prayer had been said the body was lowered over the side into the sea.

There was a moment's silence. Then came the captain's orders, "Hoist the flag!" and "Trim sails!" The main yard swung around to its former position, the wind filled the sails, and the *Pizarro* sped ahead through a green carpet of seaweed and algae.

Alexander took Aimé aside. "I think it'll be best if we leave the ship at Cumaná."

Aimé agreed immediately. They did not know it, but this decision saved their lives. The *Pizarro* was bound for Cuba, where the black plague raged at the time, killing almost all new arrivals.

52

On July 16 the town of Cumaná, in northeast Venezuela, with its castle between two clumps of coconut palms, lay before them. At nine o'clock in the morning, after forty-one days at sea, the *Pizarro* dropped anchor in the harbor.

Cumaná and Caracas

BROWN pelicans, pink flamingos, and silver-white herons swarmed in countless numbers on the beach, which was lined with coconut palms and giant tamarinds. The air seemed to glow in the heat, while a blazing sun cast an indescribable brightness over the landscape.

South America was bidding them welcome.

For the first few days Alexander and Aimé walked around as in a dream, amazed by the copper-brown skins of the Indians, the brilliant plumage of the birds, and the brightly colored fish in the sea. At the sight of the huge blossoms, some as large as dinner plates and overpoweringly scented, Aimé could only stammer, "Where to start, where make a beginning . . ."

The two friends spent their first evening in the new continent with a hospitable family who lived by the river and entertained them by moonlight, not in a room or a garden but right in the water. Chairs were put in a shallow part of the river and the bare feet of the guests dangled in the water while they smoked a special kind of cigar to keep the mosquitoes away. Occasionally dolphins frolicking about near by startled Aimé when they spouted jets of water.

The conversation was mostly about the terrible earthquake that three years before had almost completely destroyed Cumaná, one of Spain's oldest settlements in South America. The hosts described how screaming natives ran about the quaking streets, which undulated like waves, and how later the whole town was lifted into the air by a subterranean explosion. The Indians, thinking that the world had come to an end and was being created afresh, performed one of their ancient traditional dances during the night of the disaster.

Alexander made careful notes of these eyewitness reports about the earthquake. Later on, volcanic activity in Venezuela and the northern part of South America generally was to occupy him a good deal.

The two friends rented a roomy house, which Aimé quickly filled to the eaves with plant specimens, while Alexander established himself on the roof with his astronomical instruments.

The plant collection grew larger and larger, and whole notebooks were filled with long columns of figures relating to observations about the sun, the moon, and the planet Jupiter. Specimens of every kind—mother-of-pearl shells, mussels, beetles, butterflies, and plants in a bewildering variety—were packed into crates for dispatch to museums and botanical gardens in Europe; and, on top of all this, Alexander also found time to survey the coastline and to correct the three-hundred-year-old inaccuracies that he had noticed in the sea charts of the *Pizarro* before they landed.

For days they roamed about the surrounding countryside amassing new treasures for their collections. Led by their reliable scout, who was a Guayaqui Indian, they penetrated into the mountainous region of eastern Venezuela, where they made their first acquaintance with the virgin forest.

They walked beneath giant trees whose trunks were completely overgrown with green layers of lianas, orchids, and pepper vines. They saw the bottle-shaped nests of tropical thrushes, the tracks of pumas or cougars, and wonderfully colored butterflies.

Two patiently plodding mules carried their provisions and their instruments as they climbed along perilous paths into the mountains, the hunting ground of the deadly jaguar. There they came upon a great cave. Its entrance, sixty feet high, was carved out of solid rock, covered with flowering vines and exotic orchids. A broad brook came splashing out of the cave. Palms and exotic trees grew even inside the entrance. The vegetation stopped only in the dark interior where no light penetrated.

A strange screeching noise met them in the darkness, and the Indian guides kindled torches to light the way. They had advanced about two hundred yards into the cave when the shrill screeching rose to a deafening uproar. Ghostlike creatures seemed to be rustling about over their heads. The Indians tied their torches to long poles, to throw light on the tall roof of the cave, and there they saw birds the size of chickens staring down at them out of thousands of nooks and crannies. These birds, called guacharos or oilbirds, used the cave as their breeding ground and, so the Indians believed, watched over the souls of the dead.

When Aimé shot two of the birds, an unimaginable turmoil broke loose. In tens of thousands the feathered inhabitants of the cave dropped out of their nests and swarmed about the heads of the intruders. The Indian guides trembled with fear, and neither threats nor entreaties would induce them to go farther inside.

Only once a year, on Midsummer night, would the Indians venture into the cave by themselves. Then, and then only, the

evil spirits were said to be powerless. The young men would poke into the nests with long branches to fetch down the young chicks that could not yet fly. Once on the ground, the young birds, plump as geese fattened for the market, were killed and dragged to the entrance, where their fat was drained off over an open fire. This much prized semiliquid fat would keep for more than a year without going rancid.

It was hardly surprising that the Indians connected these strange birds in some way with evil spirits and the dead. No guacharo was ever seen outside in daylight. They lived their whole lives in the impenetrable darkness of the cave and in this perpetual night managed to find their way about without once dashing their heads against the tangle of stalactites that hung from the roof. No mother bird ever failed to find her own nest among the thousands of identical nooks and crannies.

Only in modern times has it been discovered that the guacharos get their bearings entirely by ear. When they fly about they utter, apart from their hoarse screechings, a series of rapid high-pitched sounds that reverberate from the surrounding walls and obstacles. By means of these sound-waves the birds are able to navigate their flight.

Alexander was the first naturalist to describe this extraordinary bird; he gave it its scientific name, *Steatornis caripensis,* and made drawings of the two specimens that Aimé had shot.

In the evening of that day, when it began to look like rain, they heard the gruesome wailing of red howling monkeys. As in a choir, there was a leader who began the dismal concert, whereupon the rest of the choir, made up of females and baby monkeys, joined in with their higher voices. Their din could be heard over a distance of three miles.

Alexander watched the monkeys closely and then said to Aimé in a puzzled voice, "Isn't it strange that the more monkeys resemble human beings, the more miserable they seem to be? Apparently they lose their good humor and liveliness when they develop their brains!"

Back in Cumaná fresh adventures awaited the two friends.

Walking along the seashore, Alexander discussed with Aimé the preparations for their journey into the unknown wilderness of the Orinoco. They were so deep in conversation they did not notice a figure emerge from behind a large patch of cacti.

This was a sambo, a half-breed—part Negro and part Indian—and a giant of a man. In his fist he carried a cudgel of palmwood with which he intended to crack the skull of the first white man he could find, because he had had a quarrel with a European and been dismissed from his job.

A crunching in the sand made Alexander turn around. Before him stood the huge sambo, naked to the waist, with the cudgel raised to strike, the whites of his eyes bulging with rage.

Uttering a warning cry, Alexander threw himself to the ground and the blow struck only the air. Aimé, preoccupied with the problem of how in the world he could get enough

58

blotting paper in Cumaná to dry and pack all the plants he meant to collect on the Orinoco, never dreamed that the sambo's cudgel could be intended for him. He was just about to step aside politely and give the snorting maniac the right of way when the cudgel cracked down on his temple. He collapsed, unconscious, while the sambo, taking Aimé's hat in token of his victory, marched off unconcernedly.

Alexander leaped to his friend's side and shook him by the shoulder, thinking the blow might have killed him, but Aimé came to quickly. As a Frenchman he naturally wanted to pay the sambo back for this unprovoked attack, and as a scientist he was indignant at having been so rudely interrupted in his thinking.

Before Alexander realized what was happening, Aimé had got to his feet and was racing after his attacker, whom he had spotted in a field of Opuntia cacti. Alexander followed him.

The sambo began to run, but Aimé, quick on his feet and not giving a thought to the fact that he was quite unarmed, caught him and tripped him up. As the giant stumbled and fell, Aimé was on top of him in a flash, pommeling the sambo's naked chest with his fists. But the giant shook him off with a single push and by the time Alexander appeared on the scene a razor-sharp knife glinted in the sambo's hand. There was no doubt now who would get the better of the fight.

At this moment a group of Spanish merchants, taking an evening walk, shouted to them. The sambo took flight and diappeared behind the cacti.

"Let him go," implored Alexander, but the sight of the knife had outraged Aimé's sense of fair play and brought his fury to boiling point. With a leap almost like that of a wild beast, he stormed into the thicket of cacti behind which the

59

sambo was sheltering. Long thorns buried themselves in Aimé's arms, thighs, and back as he thrashed about to clear a way.

The sambo, frightened by Aimé's cries of rage and pain, and thinking he was being pursued by a whole army, fled to a dilapidated chicken house next to a native hut. Here Aimé overpowered him and, with the help of Alexander and the Spanish merchants, took the defeated madman to the police.

After that Aimé collapsed. Alexander carried him, shaking with fever, off to bed. But the blow of the cudgel had caused only a slight concussion. A few days later Aimé was back with his plants again.

While Aimé was preparing a golden-yellow orchid with black markings for his herbarium, Alexander measured him with a searching look. "If you are quite fit again, we could get started for the Orinoco. Let me warn you, it will be tough going."

Aimé tucked one of the orchid's petals into place with a pair of pincers. "I am as fit as a howling monkey," he announced and carefully covered the delicate blossom with a sheet of blotting paper.

"Remember, we are going into country where no white man has ever set foot. The jungle, the animals, the climate—everything will be against us."

"Didn't I finish off the sambo?" asked Aimé in a hurt voice; and to show that he had his strength back he lifted up a crateful of specimens that was destined for the Minister for Foreign Affairs in Madrid. "As far as I am concerned, we can start today."

When Alexander returned after midday, he found Aimé all packed and ready. Their luggage was carried to the harbor and an Indian was engaged to take them in his open boat to La Guaira.

Toward evening the Indian hoisted a triangular sail, and their boat glided silently down the river to the sea. Along the banks, glowworms formed myriads of sparkling garlands that were reflected in the smooth water. Swarms of porpoises followed the wake of the boat. Whenever their broad fins broke the surface, a flash of phosphorescent light darted over the waves. At times these flashes were so bright that they seemed to come from a fire at the bottom of the sea.

When they reached the harbor of La Guaira the two friends transferred their luggage to pack mules and set out for Caracas, the capital of Venezuela, along the high mountain pass between the summits of the Silla ridge and the jagged crest of the massive Cerro de Avila.

Below them lay Caracas. Alexander was surprised to find strawberries, vines, and European fruit trees growing side by side with banana plants, orange trees, and coffee bushes.

They took lodgings for a while in the highest part of Caracas, from which they could overlook the town. Perhaps Alexander had a premonition of the terrible fate in store for this city, for he thought the landscape looked gloomy and foreboding despite its beauty. Some years later, on Easter Thursday in 1812, an earthquake completely destroyed Caracas, and twelve thousand people were buried beneath its ruins.

Across the Savanna

ENDLESSLY the savanna stretched out before them. There was not a breath of air, and the sun had long since scorched the last remaining blade of grass. Before the rainy season, the ground was parched like a desert and crisscrossed by crevices; and here and there pillars of whirling sand would rise up in the deathly silence.

Aimé and Alexander found shelter from the fierce sun underneath a stunted palm with withered leaves. Half asleep, Alexander was dreaming of the sweet milk of a cow tree which he had drunk a few days earlier straight from the trunk. It was late afternoon when he suddenly jumped up and announced, "I can hear cows mooing."

"You've got a touch of the sun," said Aimé with a sigh.

"No, get up, there must be a ranch near by."

They mounted their mules and rode off in the direction of a long dust cloud that hovered low on the horizon above the broiling plain.

"It's a *fata morgana*," * declared Aimé. His tongue was swollen from thirst, and the fine sand coating his face was making his skin smart.

* *fata morgana*—a mirage.

62

The mules quickened their step and Alexander said soothingly, "I bet you we shall be bathing tonight."

Aimé looked at him sideways. "You have got sunstroke," he said, but Alexander persisted. "There is water hereabout. Use your imagination a little. In four to six weeks, when the rains come, this dusty wilderness will turn overnight into a green meadow."

With a sweep of his hand, Alexander pictured the scene. "The grass shoots up, mimosa is in bloom, and in the swamps water snakes and crocodiles emerge from their dugouts where they had been hiding during the drought in a trance resembling death. Rivers begin to swell and animals who the day before were dying from thirst are turned into amphibious creatures. Part of the savanna becomes a huge sea. Mares with their foals take refuge on the high-lying banks that stand out of the water like islands, but every day the dry ground gets smaller, and for lack of grazing land the crowded animals swim about for hours feeding on the tips of pampas grass that show above the water. Many foals are drowned while others are devoured by crocodiles."

Aimé panted for air, half choked by the sand in his throat. But suddenly his eyes opened wide with excitement and he shouted, "A house! Look, over there!"

"Didn't I tell you?" said Alexander smugly. "Now we'll each drink a jugful of milk and I'll go on with my story."

They reached the ranch, where an old Negro slave crawled out of a shady corner and asked them what he could do for them. He was alone; his master was out in the savanna with the cattle.

"So you have cattle?" asked Alexander as he slipped out of his saddle.

"Four thousand head," the man replied proudly.

With a triumphant look at Aimé, Alexander asked for a

jug of milk. But the old man stared dumfounded at this request.

"You gentlemen ever been to the llanos before?" he asked politely.

"What's that to do with our thirst?" demanded Alexander.

"Plenty," replied the man. "In the dry season no cow in the llanos gives milk."

"Then bring water," ordered Alexander. Aimé chuckled. As they unloaded the mules, Alexander expected Aimé to make some cutting remark about the promised milk, but he was far too thirsty to think of one.

The old slave returned with a hollowed-out coconut filled with a gray, foul-smelling liquid. Aimé held his nose and shuddered.

"But that's mud, my good man," demurred Alexander.

"We put a cloth over it and drink through it." The man covered the coconut cup with a piece of clean linen and handed it to Alexander.

With a meaningful look at Aimé, Alexander took it and drank, though it nearly made him sick. Perhaps it was as well he did not know then that for months to come they would be drinking muddy water filtered through a cloth.

"Here, your turn," he said as he pressed the coconut into Aimé's hand. Then, turning to the old man, who had not moved a muscle while he had watched him drinking, he added, "Now fetch a bucket for the mules."

"A bucket? We have no buckets!" The man was aghast at the idea.

"Well, what do your animals drink out of?"

"We chase them out into the savanna—they find their own pools."

Alexander's eyes lit up. "Can one bathe in these pools?" he

asked. The old man's mouth gaped wide, the lips twitching in helpless amazement. He had never heard of such a thing in all his life.

"Let's follow the mules and when they find a pool we'll jump in," suggested Aimé as he returned the empty coconut to the old Negro, who shook his head but kept his thoughts to himself.

The mules were turned loose, and Alexander and Aimé walked behind them with long strides until, after about a quarter of a mile, the animals found a swampy pond. Aimé pointed out that it smelled as if all the cats in South America had been drowned in it, and that even the mules did not seem keen on sampling it. Alexander climbed down the steep bank and tried the water with his hand. "Wonderful, quite warm!" he called back.

Aimé pulled his shirt over his head, slipped out of his boots, and leaped into the stagnant pool. Alexander followed a few seconds later. "Heaven . . ." began Aimé, but the word half stuck in his throat when he heard an ominous splashing noise behind him. In the same instant Alexander yelled, "Crocodiles!"

They were out of their bathing pool in double-quick time and, grabbing their clothes, raced away, their hearts in their mouths. Then they stopped and listened. There wasn't a sound.

They put on their clothes and started back to the ranch house, laughing like schoolboys. "You had this coming to you after your great tale about the rainy season," teased Aimé.

They walked on and on; it became dark and still there was no sign of the ranch. Alexander looked at his watch. "But that's impossible, we've been walking for more than an hour. We are lost!" he exclaimed.

65

They wandered about till nightfall. At times it seemed as if they could see a fire on the horizon, but it only turned out to be the light of a rising star enlarged by the night mist.

"Are there jaguars in the savanna?" inquired Aimé anxiously.

"Oh, they aren't so very dangerous," Alexander reassured him. "Snakes are much worse, and this place is crawling with them." At that, Aimé began to lift his legs higher with every step.

"There is no point in wandering about any longer," decided Alexander after a while. "I suggest we camp for the night under this palm." They trampled the dry ground underneath the tree to make sure it was free of snakes and then settled down.

High above their heads they could see the Southern Cross. Raising his head, Alexander looked up at it. "Do you remember when we saw it first half a year ago?"

Aimé nodded. "We had the epidemic on board. I can tell you now, I felt very apprehensive about that," admitted Alexander.

"And yet you argued that man must achieve everything by his own efforts. You scoffed at luck and said you would rely only on your scientific knowledge."

"I still stick to that," asserted Alexander.

Aimé rubbed his stubbly chin. "As for me, I could use a little bit of luck right now."

Alexander's head jerked up. "Listen!"

"What now—more cows?"

"No, a horse." They shouted as loud as they could and the sound of muffled hoofs came nearer.

Out of the darkness loomed the figure of a rider, an Indian, with a spear raised in his fist. "Who are you?" he demanded. It took some time to convince the man that they had

66

merely lost their way and were not horse thieves. He was a gaucho from the ranch and led them back there. Exhausted, they fell like two sacks into the sweet corn straw and slept.

It was two o'clock in the morning when Alexander put his hand on Aimé's shoulder to wake him. "Get up, lazy-bones, we want to be in Calabozo by midday."

Aimé sighed. Ever since he had first known Alexander he had wondered how his friend managed with so little sleep. For a while he kept a record of the actual time Alexander spent in bed each night; it was rarely more than four hours, while he himself liked to roll up like a hedgehog at night and sleep soundly until the sun was up next morning.

As they rode over the vast plain under the stars, Aimé managed to catch up on some of the sleep he had missed. His mule was a docile animal, used to the way, and it took care not to stumble and disturb its rider's snooze.

Alexander was riding on ahead. An early morning mirage had put two rising suns on the horizon, one on top of the other. The ground over which they were riding was covered with short grass, and herds of cattle and horses were grazing in palm groves. Scattered among the cows were peaceful little groups of deer.

Aimé, now wide-awake after his sleep, was fascinated to observe how some of the animals seemed to be floating with their feet in mid-air, while those next to them were standing on firm ground. Small groves of palm trees appeared to have come away from their roots and to hover suspended above the landscape. Several times they thought they could see towers and hills on the horizon. These dissolved into thin air as they drew nearer. Their uncanny optical illusions were the result of refraction of the rays of light due to the marked difference in temperature between the individual layers of air.

A flaming-hot wind thick with dust swept over the savanna. The mules had a hard time to keep going, but by midday they reached Calabozo and a hospitable hacienda. Now they could even finish the baths of the previous night which had been so abruptly cut short.

"You should be grateful it was only crocodiles that drove you away," said the owner of the hacienda.

"Thank you kindly! What could be worse than crocodiles?" asked Aimé jokingly.

"Electric eels, for instance," replied the Spaniard. "Many swamps and pools in the savanna are full of them. We call them *trembladores,* the trembling ones. The electric shocks these eels communicate can stun a horse. Many an unsuspecting bather has drowned, paralyzed by such a shock."

Aimé shuddered. Alexander, however, wanted to know at once where he could get one of these eels. The rancher called an Indian.

"*Trembladores,* they are in every pond," he declared.

"Catch me one and you shall have a piaster," promised Alexander.

The Indian's eyes opened wide. A piaster was the price of a two-year-old ox in the llanos. He disappeared at once. Alexander unpacked his electrical instruments in readiness for the eel, but in the evening the Indian returned shamefaced and empty-handed. "It was too difficult to catch one."

Next day Alexander doubled the prize money to two piasters—for that an untamed horse could be bought. Six Indians set out and brought back a half-dead eel. Alexander began his experiments, but he might as well have tested a broomstick for electricty. Aimé pulled it by the tail and said, "Shame on you! You might have become famous and you behave like a pickled herring."

"Tomorrow we'll go ourselves," declared Alexander. "I am going to catch a nice fresh eel if it's the last thing I do."

68

Early next morning they rode to a near-by village. An Indian took them to a stream which, in the dry season, had turned into a pool of mud. Around it grew flowering tamarinds and palms.

The Indian plopped a stone into the pool, and four or five eels, as long as a full-grown man, slithered across the mire. "How did you know that there were eels in the morass?" asked Alexander.

"We wait and listen," answered the man.

They kept still for a while and then they saw how the round mouth of an eel pushed through the surface of the mud, audibly drawing in air, and disappeared again.

"They betray themselves when they come up for air," explained the Indian, imitating the sucking noise.

In various parts of the pool the heads of eels were now coming up; they breathed and vanished.

"But how do we get hold of one of the slippery creatures?" wondered Aimé.

"Make them drowsy by driving some horses in among them," suggested the Indian.

"That's a novel idea, using horses for a sedative!" said Aimé.

The Indian rode out into the savanna and, with the help of other gauchos, rounded up about thirty wild horses and mules. Amid much tumult and shouting, the animals were driven into the pool.

As soon as the first horse had tumbled in, the electric eels wriggled out of the mud and surfaced.

The Indians, armed with long sticks, stationed themselves all around the bank, some even climbing the surrounding trees, whose branches stretched out over the pool. They yelled and lashed out at the horses as they tried to escape from the pool.

69

The eels pressed against the horses' flanks and discharged their electricity, stunning some of the animals so that they collapsed. Others reared up on their hind legs, frothing at the mouth and snorting. Glazed with fear, their eyes bulged out of their heads as their legs went lame from the electric shocks; some managed to reach the banks, where they sank exhausted onto the sand.

As the desperate battle continued in the broiling pool, the eels began to grow noticeably weaker. Gradually the horses and mules became quieter, showing less fear and only twitching occasionally when they received a faint shock in a particularly sensitive part.

Now the eels came wriggling out onto the banks, and within a short time the Indians had captured five.

"They are stunned; they have spent their strength," said the gauchos.

But one especially powerful eel lashed about furiously in the sand while two Indians tried to slip a rope over its head. "Why be so cautious?" grumbled Alexander. "It can do no more harm," and he put his foot on the writhing, maddened creature. Instantly he received such a shock that he nearly collapsed. He screamed with pain and for hours afterward his knees shook and all his joints ached. The Indians had a hearty laugh at his expense.

Alexander took no notice of his pains. He spent the rest of the day with Aimé examining the dangerous creatures. The two took turns testing the eels by allowing themselves to be shocked in different parts of their bodies, and every time the involuntary jerk of their muscles was followed by a painful numbness.

They discovered that the organs which contained the electric charge were located along either side of the eel's spine and that they consisted of about six thousand individual cells

70

connected in series so as to form a powerful electric battery.

When Aimé went to bed that evening he felt as if he had been felling trees all day. He was so weak that he could barely lift his arms, and for once Alexander allowed him to sleep late next morning.

Two specimen eels were added to their collection and accompanied them on their way to San Fernando de Apure, on one of the many tributaries of the Orinoco, whence they would continue their journey by water.

In the Heart of the Jungle

IN THE short grass of a hillock overlooking the Apure, a jaguar waited for Alexander to come nearer. The rays of the sun piercing through the tangle of foliage flickered over the black spots on the animal's golden-yellow skin, and the black tip of his tail twitched nervously.

Alexander was absorbed by a huge school of giant crocodiles all coiled together and asleep on the riverbank. They were the biggest he had ever seen, some of them three times the size of a man. Crocodile birds, small snow-white creatures similar to plovers, were walking about on the crocodiles' horny backs picking flies and maggots out of the mud crust that caked the scales.

Taking care not to wake the reptiles, Alexander cautiously circled around the giant coil, his eyes fixed on the crocodiles. Nearer and nearer he came to the jaguar.

A flock of flamingos passed overhead, wild bees hummed, and huge butterflies of fabulous colors flitted about the orchids. Parrots and parakeets made a commotion in a thicket close by.

Aimé was on the riverbank with the Indians, who were roasting the juicy haunch of a water hog over an open fire.

The jaguar's amber-colored eyes shone in anticipation—his human prey was walking straight into his clutches. With a couple of leaps he could be at his victim's throat, but he waited.

A glitter in the sand attracted Alexander's attention. Could it be gold? He bent down to pick up some of the tiny fragments. It was mica—a crystallized mineral that splits up into very thin small leaves. As he raised himself he saw the fresh tracks of the jaguar in the sand. His eyes followed them and met those of the jungle cat!

For a second his heart stopped beating. He had no rifle—not even a knife; the only piece of equipment on him was his compass.

Thoughts raced through his head at lightning speed. What was it the Indians had said? Face to face with a jaguar, the thing to do is to go on walking and not pay the slightest attention to him.

But how could a man go on walking when his knees were knocking together from fright, and the trees in front of his eyes seemed to be going round in circles?

With a great effort Alexander pulled himself together. He forced himself to make a half-turn and put one foot in front of the other. Hardly daring to breathe, he stealthily moved forward. To look back meant certain death, and yet every nerve in his body made him want to turn his head. He could feel the jaguar's eyes watching behind him, thoughtfully following his progress.

The sweat ran down his forehead and into his eyes, smarting like acid. He wanted to raise his hand to wipe it off, but no! Never move a muscle of either arm—on this point the Indians had been most insistent—and never run.

There seemed no end to the sand. Alexander tried unsuccessfully to glance to his left, where the crocodiles had been sleeping. Who was to know that they had not awakened and were now creeping toward him?

The nearest bushes on the riverbank seemed an eternity away. With all his senses alert, he was able to discern a slight disturbance on the far side of the river where a herd of water hogs were swimming across the water.

At most he had taken ten steps so far, but it seemed as if he had been walking for years. Had the beast moved? Was it ready to jump?

As he walked, the events of the past few days flashed before his mind's eye. At San Fernando they had climbed into an Indian boat amid thunder, lightning, and a cloudburst. The rainy season had begun in February and Aimé was jubilant.

"Hurrah, no more of this infernal dust! I feel like a human being again. Nothing that lies ahead can possibly be as bad as this desert has been," he had said.

They had covered the boat aft with a temporary deck against the rain and had constructed rectangular frames out of brazilwood on which they nailed tightly stretched skins to serve as tabletops and benches.

A Franciscan friar, who was helping them with their preparations, had stocked the boat with chickens, eggs, bananas, cassava roots whose starchy flour is used for making bread, maize, cocoa, and oranges—enough provisions for a month of voyaging along the rivers through uninhabited jungle.

"Take care not to go too near to the Brazilian border," the friar had warned. "The Portuguese are in power there and your Spanish passports would make them very suspicious." As a parting gift he had brought aboard a cask of local sherry.

Alexander had been touched by the friar's help and, thanking him warmly, he had tried to calm his fears: "My only ambition is to prove beyond a shadow of doubt that the two great river basins of the Orinoco and the Amazon are linked to one another. We plan to go down the Apure until it joins the Orinoco, then upstream to the point where the Casiquiare enters the Orinoco, then along the Casiquiare until it reaches the Rio Negro, the tributary of the Amazon. If we succeed in this we shall be the first to bring back reliable charts and accurate information about this vast river network. . . ."

"As well as a few crates of plants that I hope no one will ever have heard of before," Aimé had added with a triumphant gleam in his eye.

"Take good care, and God be with you!" had been the friar's parting wish.

The four naked Indians had pushed their oars into the water and the steersman, who differed from the crew only in

75

wearing coarse linen trousers and an ancient dilapidated hat, had put the tiller about.

The bulldog puppy that Alexander had brought along barked a last farewell to the friar as they shot downstream toward the Orinoco.

The Apure was more than three hundred yards wide and its banks were lined with dense thickets behind which loomed the jungle. Curassows with combs like turkeys strutted pompously among the bushes, panthers came to drink in the river, and crocodiles swarmed in the water.

The Indian oarsmen had taught Aimé and Alexander the

rudiments of jungle lore. If attacked by a crocodile, they must poke their fingers into its eyes. Even when there were no crocodiles about, bathing was not safe because the river swarmed with piranhas, bloodthirsty fish that are seldom seen but appear in thousands as soon as they scent living flesh in the water.

Against the mosquitoes, the Indians knew of no remedy—the *señores* would soon see, or rather feel, for themselves.

Oh, it had all seemed like paradise at first. In the early morning the white bellbirds rang their chimes from giant mulberry trees, while the orange and black troupials accompanied them on the flute. Macaws, whose feathers were sky-blue on top and canary-yellow underneath, twittered and chattered in the trees, and all around the doves were cooing.

Docile tapirs rooted in the mire with their long snouts, white-lipped peccaries ganged up together to wallow in the river mud, and water hogs, the world's largest rodents, stared vacantly at the swiftly passing current.

Yes, it had all seemed like paradise until the moment his eyes met those of the jaguar. Was the beast still on the hillock or was it creeping up behind him?

Alexander reached the thicket; he squeezed through the dense scrub along a narrow animal trail and heaved a deep sigh of relief. In that instant a heavy paw descended on his shoulder like a cudgel.

Alexander sank to his knees.

"Hey, there!" a voice called. "The pork is done to a turn."

Looking up, he saw that it was not the jaguar's paw but Aimé's hand that lay on his shoulder. At first Aimé laughed at having startled Alexander, but when he saw his friend's face drained of every drop of blood, he asked in alarm, "What's up?"

Alexander pointed with his eyes to the hillock along the bank. "Look up there—the jaguar."

Now it was Aimé who turned pale. "And you passed him?"

"Within a few yards," said Alexander.

Aimé was lost in admiration. "I take my hat off to you. I'd never have been able to do it. Quickly, let's get our guns."

But when they returned with their guns, it was too late. The king of the jungle had left his observation post.

Later that day on their way downstream they passed a herd of grazing sea cows. "Stupid creatures!" remarked Aimé.

"Maybe, but very interesting," replied Alexander. "They are not unlike whales, although they look more like seals. When we get the chance we must dissect one of them. They weep real tears, which are sold as magic potions at a high price. They'll make any girl fall in love with you."

"You'd better get yourself some," teased Aimé. "As for me, I don't need them!"

That night the Indians tied the boat at the riverbank under a huge thorn tree and lit a fire. But its glow attracted the entire crocodile and dolphin population of the neighborhood. Alexander, who felt that he had had enough adventure for one day, made them put out the fire.

Now the mosquitoes descended on them in thick clouds. They were of a particularly vicious species with extra-long sucking stingers, or proboscises, which went right through blankets and clothes and stung like fire. Hundreds of the poisonous insects were swatted to death, only to be immediately replaced by thousands of others who came hurtling out of the darkness for fresh attacks on their victims. They made all hope of sleep impossible.

Besides, the jungle was alive with noises of every kind; musk ducks screeched on the water, a sloth howled in the distance, and apes shrieked and caterwauled in all the treetops. After a while the bulldog puppy joined the concert and even a little cat began to miaow.

"Jaguar!" shouted the Indian steersman. Alexander shot out of his hammock. Since it was a mother taking her cub to the river to drink, Alexander would not allow the Indian to shoot her.

It was midnight before Alexander again sank back into his hammock, determined that nothing would keep him from his sleep for the rest of the night, not even the fiendish mosquitoes.

Suddenly the little dog gave out a terrified yelp. By the time Aimé and Alexander had dug themselves out of their blankets, gigantic bats flapped back and forth over their heads and even emerged from underneath their hammocks. One of them attached itself to the puppy's head and began to suck its blood.

Finally the bat let go of its victim and disappeared into the night. Examining the terrified puppy by candlelight, Alexander found that the wound was tiny and could hardly hurt. The little dog whimpered pitifully and snuggled up against Aimé's chest.

"Shame on you," scolded Alexander. "Leoncillo, Balboa's dog, would never have made such a fuss."

"Perhaps if we call him Leoncillo," suggested Aimé, "he will feel obliged to show a little more courage in the future and bite the bats instead of letting them bite him."

So they christened the puppy Leoncillo and drank a glass of sherry in his honor, although Leoncillo didn't appear too eager to step into his famous namesake's shoes.

They continued their long river journey. On reaching the Orinoco in March, 1800, Alexander measured its width from one bank to the other and found that it extended over two and a half miles, although the water level was at a low point after the long drought. During the rainy season the river would spread out over six or seven miles. Compared with the Amazon, which thundered like a mighty ocean through the virgin forest, the Orinoco, wide as it was, seemed hardly more than a brook. If all the rivers of Europe from the Volga to the Manzanarez were combined in one bed, they would still not be a match for the Amazon—that giant among the world's rivers.

Still, for a start, the Orinoco was impressive enough. With a fresh wind at their back they sailed upstream toward a group of islands where turtles had congregated to lay their eggs. The annual forgathering of these huge creatures, each weighing about a hundred pounds, was well under way. Alexander estimated that there were nearly a million turtles which in the course of one night might each lay as many as a hundred eggs in the loose sand. All along the beaches as far as the eye could reach, the eggs were arranged in neat hollows covered with sand.

No sooner had the hard-working turtles finished their laying than the equally hard-working Indians came along to dig up the eggs and carry them in baskets to their camps. There the eggs were put in wooden troughs filled with water, then crushed with shovels. The yolks, floating on the surface like cream, were skimmed off and boiled to extract the oil.

Although hundreds of Indians were busily collecting, the sand at Alexander's feet swarmed with tiny baby turtles making for the water at top speed. Laughing Indian children chased them, and herons and vultures devoured many of them. In the river, crocodiles lay in wait for others. Mother turtles fell prey to jaguars, which turned the defenseless creatures over on their backs and then scooped the juicy flesh out of the shell with their claws.

Sickened by the sight of so much slaughter, Alexander went to lie down in the boat with Leoncillo. By the afternoon Aimé too had had enough and called the crew together to set sail. The men carried baskets filled with eggs and young turtles, which they planned to eat on the way. The helmsman tacked upstream in the moonlight until they came to a bare, sandy island where they went ashore for the night.

They ate their supper sitting on large turtle shells. Alexander was more than usually lost in his own thoughts. They had been only three days on the Orinoco. A journey of three months lay before them.

It was a sultry night, and since there were no trees to which they could tie their hammocks, they lay on skins spread out over the warm sand. The brightly burning campfire did nothing to discourage the mosquitoes.

A muffled bellow drove the men out of their beds and started Leoncillo to whimpering. Jaguars had swum across to the island to prowl around the campfire.

"The big cats are always at their most insolent when the turtles are laying eggs," explained the steersman.

"Fetch the rifles," ordered Alexander.

But the powder had become wet during a squall on the trip up the river.

"There's nothing to be done," said Aimé. "We shall have to put up with our visitors."

"Well, we have Leoncillo to defend us," joked Alexander.

The jaguars began a night-long siege, snarling and bellowing all around the camp.

"Let's go to sleep," urged Aimé. There was nothing else to do. Wrapped in their blankets with Leoncillo snuggled down between them, Aimé and Alexander fell asleep in a few minutes.

Next morning the puppy was missing. They searched the beach and called, but he was not to be found. One of the jaguars must have carried him off while they slept.

"Brave little Leoncillo," said Aimé softly. "The beasts took him instead of us. He must have wandered out during the night and they pounced on him."

"It often happens," said the steersman, "that the older jaguars snatch an animal right out of the middle of a camp and break its neck so that it won't cry out. Who knows what might have happened if they had not got hold of the dog?"

River Journey in a Tree-Boat

WHEN they reached the waterfalls of the Orinoco, the steersman became worried. "No one can get through these rapids," he said.

"But you have been boasting that you are braver than all the boatmen of South America put together," remonstrated Alexander.

"That I am, and my knife will prove it to anybody who doubts it," said the Indian, fingering the broad blade of his machete, a sharp bush-knife as long as his forearm.

"We must go on," urged Alexander, but the steersman pointed his chin toward the bank where a few Indian huts could be seen. "The *señores* will find a missionary there with whom they might like to speak," he suggested.

Turning to Aimé, Alexander said in French, "This is the exact spot where Sir Walter Raleigh had to turn back after making four attempts to get up the Orinoco. It must be fate!"

"Sir Walter Raleigh?"

"Yes, he wanted to convince Queen Elizabeth that the Spanish colonies could be conquered from the Orinoco. Had he succeeded in this Shakespeare might have written a play about Huáscar, who was almost the last Inca."

83

"And what did Raleigh hope to find here?"

"The legendary land of gold, *El Dorado,* as the Spaniards say. He wrote to his Queen that every mountain, every stone in the jungles of the Orinoco shone as if it were made of precious metal. If it wasn't gold, it must at least be goldstone, he believed."

"I haven't seen any of it so far," remarked Aimé. He couldn't know that a hundred and fifty years after this journey the richest mineral deposits in the world would be discovered along the Orinoco.

Alexander and Aimé went to see the missionary. They found him sitting together with other monks under a palm tree. All wore blue habits and long, venerable beards.

"So you want to get to the Rio Negro?" the missionary asked, looking searchingly at Alexander. "Fifty years ago the Spanish government sent its last expedition there, three hundred and twenty-five men, to solve the riddle of the jungle and find out if the waters of the Orinoco and the Amazon join. Only thirteen men came back, starved, sick with fever, and half mad. They had not found the missing link between the Orinoco and the Rio Negro."

"Yet Father Ramón did reach the Rio Negro by following the Casiquiare," asserted Alexander.

"Isn't it enough that one man got there?"

"No, sir," contradicted Alexander politely but firmly. "We need scientific proof and exact information instead of mere assertion."

The missionary shook his head. "You leave your homeland and come here to be eaten alive by mosquitoes so that you can survey a land that doesn't even belong to you! Look at the monks here, they all have malaria."

Alexander was not to be shaken in his determination. Despite misgivings, the missionary went with Aimé and Alexander to the riverbank and selected a canoe for them. "No other craft will take you through the rapids," he said.

The canoe was a hollowed-out tree trunk, about thirty-nine feet long and barely three feet wide.

Aimé looked at it skeptically. In this slender shell, which looked more like a water trough for animals than a boat, was he to stow away his priceless herbarium, his irreplaceable plant press, the cases filled with every kind of specimen, their valuable instruments, and food? What if it capsized?

But worse was to come.

"Since you are naturalists," the missionary said, "I'd like to show you some of my rare animals." He took them to the mission house, where they discovered a whole menagerie of animals in the courtyard. There were rare golden rockbirds in cages made of the stalks of palm leaves; capuchin monkeys with the innocent faces of little children; weeping monkeys, graceful little widow monkeys all black except for a ring of pure white around the face.

"I should like to take some of these animals with me on our trip," said Alexander.

"What!" Aimé was aghast at the suggestion.

"We should have the chance to get to observe them in the boat. As far as I know, they have never been scientifically studied before."

"Don't forget that a tree-boat isn't a Noah's Ark!" exclaimed Aimé, horrified.

"Oh, there is more room than you think," the missionary assured him good-naturedly, whereupon, without further ado, Alexander selected a dozen bird and monkey cages with their inmates.

Speechless, Aimé stomped off in the direction of the forest.

When Alexander called after him to ask where he was going he replied curtly, "I'll just cut myself a few rare trees to load into the canoe!"

The next morning they said goodbye to the missionary. He had ordered one of his Indians to accompany them because the man spoke the languages of the tribes in the regions to which they were going. At first the Indian had been unwilling and it looked as if he would have to be forced, but when Alexander promised that he would be brought back to the mission he agreed to go of his own free will. His name, he said, was Zerepe.

Across the stern of the boat lay strong branches covered with big leaves to form a kind of bower against the sun. But this roof was so low that the two men could only lie flat underneath it or crouch uncomfortably with their backs bent. When stretched out full-length, their legs dangled in the water.

As they pushed off, the tree-boat began to sway ominously and Aimé closed his eyes. When he opened them again, the boat was right out in the middle of the stream.

In the forward end the Indian oarsmen, naked from head to toe, sat hunched over their short oars, which they dipped into the water like large soup spoons.

Since it was impossible to get up and move about while the boat was afloat, there was no escaping the mosquitoes that descended on the canoe in thick clouds. Faces and hands became swollen from countless stings. Monkeys chattered in their cages and birds preened themselves, the only members of the expedition seeming to enjoy the river voyage.

Precipitous granite rocks, black as coal, hemmed in the wide river on both sides. The water splashed and sprayed over crags and boulders while the tree-boat danced and tossed like a straw in the eddying whirlpools.

86

Yet this was only the beginning. For twelve hours the Indian oarsmen fought against the might of the current and maneuvered the long canoe through narrow, navigable channels. In places where the current was too strong, they jumped onto the embattled rocks and towed the canoe behind them.

A mighty thundering noise gave warning of the approaching rapids at Atures and Maipures, where the Orinoco, hemmed in by huge rocks and granite boulders for six to seven miles, literally dissolved into a sea of foam. Here the canoe had to be unloaded, and the Indians carried first the boat and then its contents across the slippery cliffs. In some places Alexander heard the water roaring underneath his feet and above his head at the same time.

Deeper and deeper they pushed into the uninhabited wilderness. All around them lurked the hostile creatures of the jungle: pumas and black jaguars prowled about their camps at night. Crocodiles as fearsome as the mythical dragons would follow their tracks as they took measurements on the riverbanks; poisonous arrows whizzed mysteriously through the dense foliage; hissing snakes dangled from branches above their heads.

Chiggers embedded themselves in the skin between their toes and underneath their toenails. After a few days the female, bearing eggs, would swell to the size of a pea and cause abscesses which made walking an agony.

Still, the mosquitoes remained their worst enemies. Only the females sting; the males seem not to hanker after human blood, getting their nourishment from the juice of flowers. Moreover, the females are also the carriers of the dreaded malaria germ, which they introduce into the bloodstream with every sting. To escape their attacks, Alexander and Aimé dug themselves right into the sandy riverbank at night, covering their whole bodies except for their heads with sand and earth.

Whenever Aimé looked at his plant collection, he discovered some new destructive insects busily devouring the specimens. He tried camphor, turpentine, and tar, used boards treated with pitch to hang his specimen chests on branches away from the ground, but nothing would discourage the insects. He could have wept with rage when he found that five out of eight plants that he had collected under great difficulties and prepared in a tropical downpour were destroyed. Whole quantities of pressed plants had to be thrown into the river.

Trying to defend their treasures against a host of ants, the men struggled on toward the Rio Negro. For five weeks the slender tree-boat slid past impenetrable forests shrouded in interminable, desolating rain. When the sun did break through the clouds, the earth steamed like a caldron.

Their only food was rice, large ants, cassava or manioc roots, and bananas. Aimé had become reconciled to drinking river water, which was sometimes green, sometimes dark blue, and, farther on in the south, black as coffee, though wonderfully clear. He liked the black water best for there were no mosquitoes and no crocodiles in the southern regions.

Majestic palm forests flanked the Rio Negro. Toucans called shrilly from slender fruit trees, and swarms of parrots flew across the river. On the bank stood a group of wild-looking natives, eying the strangers suspiciously.

"Perhaps we can get some food from them," suggested Alexander.

Zerepe addressed the naked figures on the shore, some of whom wore apple-green stones ground to a cylindrical shape around their necks. They waited expectantly, though still on their guard, and stared with curiosity at Alexander as he stepped with stiff joints out of the boat. He was the first white man they had seen.

Zerepe asked them if they had any meat, but Alexander, whose only thought until then had been of a juicy roast of water hog, interrupted him hastily. "Ask them where they got the green stones."

The savages hid their stones in the palms of their hands and made a reply which Zerepe translated, "From the women who live without men."

"Ask them who these women are."

A lengthy conversation then ensued between Zerepe and the natives. Finally Alexander was allowed to look at the stones, which were engraved with pictures and inscriptions.

Then Zerepe translated, "They are a tribe of women who make long blowpipes for ejecting missiles, and other weapons. They live without men, but when they are out hunting and meet with Indians, they select the bravest and best-looking and take them with them for a while. Later the men must leave again, and as farewell presents the women give them blowpipes, which never miss, and these green stones. The women keep only their girl children. Boys are killed at birth."

"Where do these women live?"

The Indians pointed into the jungle. Zerepe was given one of the stones to hold and passed it on to Alexander. It was a hard, precious stone, transparent and blue-green.

"None of these Indians have tools with which to bore a hole in such a stone, let alone engrave pictures on them," said Alexander to Aimé. "They must date from a time when there was a much more highly developed civilization in this region. Francisco de Orellana wrote of it in the sixteenth century."

"Orellana, the discoverer of the Amazon?"

Alexander nodded. "That was one of the most adventurous journeys ever made by man."

"And he met these warlike women?"

"So he says. He named the Amazon after them."

"What drove him to the Amazon?"

"Hunger." Alexander looked at the amazonite stone, which seemed to light up in his hand, and continued, "As you know, Francisco de Pizarro conquered the realm of the Incas in Peru with an army of a hundred and eighty soldiers and twenty-seven horses. His brother Gonzalo was made Governor in Quito, and there he heard of a fabulous land where trees with fragrant leaves and nuts grew; a land said to be paved with gold and silver. The ruler of the land—so the legend went—had himself covered with liquid gold every morning and had it washed off again at night. During the day he walked about like a statue of burnished gold. But the way to this fabulous land was far and led through dense forest.

"Such news could not have pleased Gonzalo more. He set out at once to the east with two hundred Spanish cavalrymen in full armor, and four thousand Indians. They took with them thousands of pigs, a large herd of llamas, and blood-hounds.

"They made slow progress through the jungle that stretched endlessly before them and were frequently attacked by hostile tribes. After eight months the pigs and llamas had been eaten, and in the swampy jungle the men found nothing edible except worms, grass, and nuts. They began to slaughter the horses, then the dogs. Their Indians, natives of the Andes mountains, died in the humid climate of the plain.

"When they reached the Coca River all their provisions were exhausted and Gonzalo ordered Captain Francisco de Orellana to build a boat and go downstream in search of food. Orellana left with a crew of fifty on Christmas Day, 1540, not suspecting that he would never see his commander again.

"He drifted downstream and after nine days found food, but his men were too weak to row the boat back against the powerful current. So he decided to go on into the unknown. Somewhere to the east he hoped to reach the Atlantic Ocean.

"He and his men built another boat and went down the Napo River till at last they saw an enormous expanse of water lying before them. Was this the ocean? or not? they asked themselves in Spanish—*Marañón?*—and to this day that part of the upper Amazon is called Marañón.

"Hunger forced them to boil their belts and shoe soles to make soup, and when finally they became so weak that they could no longer stand up on their legs, they beached their boat and crawled on their hands and knees into the forest to search for edible roots and tubers. Astonished Indians took pity on them and gave them meat and fish, warning them at the same time against the warlike women who lived farther on along the river.

91

"Later the explorers took to plundering peaceful villages, and pursued by angry natives they regained their boat and continued on their way downstream until they reached the region inhabited by the legendary female tribe. Here they were hopelessly defeated. The women fought with such bravery that the Spaniards had to flee. The hull of their boat was studded with arrows like a porcupine's back.

"From then on they never ventured on land again, but kept to their boat and made do with whatever food they could fish out of the river.

"In September of 1541 they reached the Atlantic Ocean and returned to Spain. But people only laughed when they spoke of their adventures. No one else had ever been to the Amazon, so all the world was quite certain that Orellana had invented the whole thing. Not a word of his account of the three-thousand-mile voyage along a gigantic river with hundreds of tributaries was believed."

"What became of Orellana?" asked Aimé.

"His armchair critics, who had never ventured outside their four walls, never stopped accusing him of spinning a fantastic yarn. So he went to the Emperor Charles V, who ruled over both Spain and Germany, and asked to be allowed to sail once again into the Amazon country, but this time upstream from the river mouth, so that he might be able to prove his discoveries.

"Permission was granted, but Orellana had to equip his own ships for the expedition. The continuing slander of his critics made him overhasty and he started his second Amazon voyage with four worm-eaten ships. Two of them sank on the way across to South America, and the other two never got beyond the immense river delta. A mutiny among the crew, fever, and poisoned arrows brought the whole venture to a quick and terrible end. Orellana died of exhaustion and was buried under an ancient tree in the evergreen jungle."

"And what of Gonzalo Pizarro—did he find his golden King?"

"No, the jungle defeated him. Many of his soldiers died, and the few men who arrived back in Quito, sick with fever and exhausted, had nothing with them but their swords.

"To the east of the great salt mines of Zipaquirá in the eastern foothills of the Andes there is a sacred lake called Guatavita. Traces of steps, hewn out of the rock face, can still be seen there. They were probably used for ceremonial washing rites. The Indians say that gold vessels and gold dust lie at the bottom of this lake, and I believe that this is where the legendary El Dorado is to be found, not in the lagoons and rivers of Venezuela and Brazil, where later generations looked for it in vain."

Both friends fell silent for a while. More than a hundred years after their journey, Alexander's guess was proved right. In 1912 the Guatavita lake was drained and at its bottom jewelry, gold, and precious stones of fabulous value were discovered.

"After listening to what you have told me about Orellana," said Aimé, "I am all the more anxious to go farther south to the Amazon and Portuguese territory. To follow the Amazon down to its mouth would not take longer than to paddle all the way back to the Orinoco."

Alexander was inclined to agree. He too was drawn to the Amazon, for he knew that all great civilizations of the past had started on rivers, and it was tempting to imagine that one day the Amazon would be the center of a great new civilization. A virgin country with undreamed-of natural resources would attract people from all over the world.

93

"All right," he said; "let's make for the Spanish frontier fortress at San Carlos."

When they arrived there and talked to the commandant, he was horrified to hear of their intention and warned them against entering Portuguese territory.

"Your passports were issued by the Spanish government," he pointed out. "This makes you hostile foreigners in the eyes of the Portuguese, in view of the strained relations that exist at present between Spain and Portugal."

"But we are scientists; and in any case the affairs of Europe can't matter out here in the jungle," remonstrated Alexander.

"I can see that you are scientists," replied the commandant with good-natured irony. "The quarrels among European nations follow all of us into the farthest corners of the earth. Why else, do you think, would there be a Spanish fortress out here in the wilderness on the Rio Negro facing the frontier with Portuguese Brazil?

"The seriousness of the situation has made it necessary to enforce security measures on both sides. We might be attacked by Portuguese troops any day, and if it comes to open hostilities you may be taken for spies and shot. I must ask you therefore to leave the frontier region as quickly as possible."

Frustrated and angry, they departed. "Now I know why I feel so happy in the jungle," grumbled Aimé; ". . . seriousness of the situation . . . security measures . . . pshaw!"

He was much angrier than Alexander, who had not finished all the surveying he planned to do between the Rio Negro and the Orinoco. It was more for this reason than out of cautious common sense that they dropped their plan to cross over into Portuguese territory and go on to the Amazon.

But it was just as well—the decision saved them from spending at least a year as prisoners in a Brazilian fortress. Un-

94

known to them, information of their presence in the disputed frontier region had reached the authorities in Europe, and a warrant for their immediate arrest should they enter Portuguese territory had been issued. Luckily, the warrant was never executed.

Deadly Poison

In a forest clearing, fringed by palms with silvery leaves, Indians were dancing to the mournful strains of reed pipes.

"They are celebrating the *juvias* feast in honor of the Brazil-nut harvest," explained Zerepe.

Reeds of various lengths were bound together to make these pipes, on which the musicians produced haunting and wildly exciting melodies. Young and old men, deadly serious and silent, whirled around in a circle to these airs.

As the tree-boat came to rest on the riverbank, an Indian woman with straight black hair brought a basket with delicacies to welcome them.

"What charming people!" exclaimed Aimé; but when he looked in the basket his eyes bulged with horror: it was filled with roasted hands.

"Oh, they are not human hands," Zerepe assured him. "They are the hands of monkeys." An old Indian added, "Their flesh is a little darker than human flesh but it tastes just as good."

When Zerepe translated this remark, the two white men felt thoroughly sick. But Alexander's curiosity quickly got the better of his disgust, and he said to Zerepe, "Ask them if they eat human flesh."

The old man answered and Zerepe translated, "Close to the bell"—by which he meant the mission house—"we eat only what the Fathers eat, but our relatives deep in the jungle eat the flesh of human beings, of bears, and of monkeys, especially the palms of their hands."

"Had we gone on farther down the black waters of the Rio Negro instead of returning to the white waters of the Casiquiare," added Zerepe, "we should have come to a high rocky mountain beyond San Carlos. There the chief of the Manitivitano tribe, the great Cocuy, had his cave fortress. Cocuy had many wives, the most beautiful in the jungle, and he gave them as much food as they could eat. With delight in his eyes he watched them grow as fat as sea cows, and when they were fattened to his liking he had them roasted and ate them with great relish. He was the most famous chief on the Rio Negro. His sister now lives in a mission, and his son is chief of the Indians in San Carlos."

"I still don't want to take a bite of these hands," said Aimé, shuddering.

The basket was taken away and, instead, palm cabbage, which tasted like cauliflower, and dumplings made of fish-meal were served.

The Indians meanwhile carried on with their harvest dance. Between dances they drank immense quantities of spirits made of fermented manioc tubers, and swaying drunkenly on unsteady feet they then continued in great seriousness with the puppetlike motions of the dance.

A dignified-looking gentleman, who seemed less drunk than his colleagues, disappeared mysteriously from time to time into a hut from which came clouds of white steam.

"That's the poison-master," whispered Zerepe, "the curare cook."

Alexander at once stopped eating. Curare is one of the

most potent poisons known to man; it paralyzes the victim immediately and invariably kills him. European explorers had reported that only old women were used for this distilling work, which was done in strict seclusion. By the time the deadly poison was brewed, the women lay dead beside the caldron, overcome by the poisonous fumes.

Here the poison-master seemed to be walking unharmed in and out of his steaming kitchen. Was he really brewing curare? Alexander followed him into the vapor-filled hut made of palm fronds, as always unconcerned about any danger to himself. Thus he became the first scientist to learn about the brewing of curare.

The poison-master's pedantic, punctilious manners reminded Alexander of the old-fashioned apothecaries in Europe. He was a delicately built little man with a wrinkled face.

"I know," he said, "that the white man is skilled in the making of black powder, but the noise of the gun chases away any animal he may have missed." He chuckled to himself. "No, curare is better than anything you make over there on the other side of the sea. It kills silently and it never fails. Besides, it relieves pain."

The poison-master took a piece of vine which, Alexander noted, was of the strychnine family, and scraped off the bark. Then he pounded it into hairsbreadth fibers and threw them into a cone made of a rolled banana leaf. He seemed particularly proud of this cone, and Alexander had to admire it before the man would prop the rolled leaf into a ring of palm stalks and pour water into it. Slowly a yellow liquid dripped through into a big earthenware pan. The liquid was then boiled over an open fire.

"One has to taste it," said the old man, dipping his finger into the brew and licking it.

Without thinking, Alexander followed his example, but be-

fore his finger reached his mouth the poison-master's hand
encircled his wrist in an iron grip. "Only if there is no wound
in your mouth—otherwise you die," he warned sternly, letting go of Alexander's wrist.

He waited expectantly.

Alexander tried to remember whether he had a sore place
anywhere in his mouth. The poison would kill only if it entered into his bloodstream. But if he did not taste it, he would
lose face before the poison-master.

So he popped his finger into his mouth. The taste was as
bitter as gall. Alexander pulled a face. The poison-master

nodded approvingly. Now that Alexander had passed the test he could be accepted as a colleague.

"The bitterer the juice, the better the poison," the old man said, proceeding to introduce Alexander into the secrets of his trade.

Meanwhile Alexander waited for any sign of oncoming sickness. When there was none, he concluded that the reports of women dying from the fumes were mere hearsay.

To thicken the juice and make it adhere to the point of an arrow, the poison-master added a gluey plant concoction. It produced a black and sticky mixture like molasses.

Giving the brew a final stir, the poison-master asked, "Looks deadly, doesn't it?" Alexander only laughed; the stuff looked quite harmless. Whereupon the poison-master, with a mischievous grin, took a minute quantity of the black glue between his thumb and forefinger and rubbed the points of two arrows with it. Then he led Alexander outside the hut, took a blowpipe, and peered into the trees.

From high up in a giant ceiba tree, half hidden in a cluster of orchids, a *hokko*—a bird the size of a peacock—was calling "Hoo, hoo." The poison-master put the blowpipe to his lips, took aim, and blew into it.

Alexander couldn't see the arrow because it flew too quickly, but behind the orchids the *hokko* suddenly flapped its wings and then plunged like a stone to the ground. When Alexander rushed to where it had fallen, it was paralyzed and in less than two minutes was dead.

The poison-master shot the second arrow into a pig wallowing in the mud on the riverbank. The animal gave a jerk, stood up, and waddled toward the forest. All of a sudden its legs gave way; it sank to its knees, and died.

Alexander had positive proof of the terrible effectiveness of this poison.

Three Indians skinned the dead pig and took out its entrails. "We'll eat it tonight," said the poison-master.

"And the poison won't do any harm?" asked Aimé anxiously.

"There isn't a chicken along the length and breadth of the Orinoco that has not been killed by a poisoned arrow," replied the old man. "Curare is poisonous only in the blood; elsewhere it acts like a healing medicine. Our people eat it when they have a stomach-ache. Taken in this way, it cures as quickly as it kills on the point of an arrow."

When Alexander was given a little lump of curare, he asked Zerepe to collect some frogs and birds, for experimental purposes. Aimé unpacked the instruments and dissolved samples of the poison in test tubes. In a flash the jungle clearing was turned into a laboratory. Alexander wrote down observations so they might later be studied in the scientific institutions of Europe. He filled pages and pages of his notebook, which as usual lay on his knee, and at the end he wrote, "The analysis of the properties of this poison is an important task for chemistry, and more especially for medicine."

But the scientists of Europe and America neglected this task and showed little interest in curare for a century and more. Not until 1944 did American doctors discover that it was a very useful drug for surgical cases and the treatment of infantile paralysis.

"The food's ready, *Señores,*" called Zerepe. After hours of experimenting Alexander and Aimé suddenly realized that they were hungry. They washed their hands in the river and entered the hut which served as dining hall. A gruesome sight met their eyes. Drunken Indians lounged on the earth floor, and propped up along the walls, leaning forward, sat horrifying figures, dark and motionless.

They were large roasted apes, blackened by soot and

101

smoke, their dead faces bearing an uncanny resemblance to human beings. With smacking lips, the Indians were lustily gnawing away at whole arms complete with hands and fingers. It was the next thing to a cannibal feast. Sickened, Aimé fled outside and made for the back of the hut where a fire was burning. What he saw there drove away the rest of his appetite.

A skinned capuchin monkey had been put in a sitting position on the grid, and to prevent it from toppling over it was made to lean forward with its long, thin arms stretched out in front of it. As the flames licked the pitiful naked figure, the rising smoke shrouded its head.

At first glance Aimé thought it was a child crouching in the fire—it seemed to be moving in the light of the flickering flames. Then he realized it was a dead monkey.

During their long journey Aimé had had plenty of opportunity to study the menus of the various Indian tribes and to look into their cooking pots. He had seen Indians roasting large fatted ants, and centipedes looking like sausages with legs attached; he had seen them eat parrots, lizards, and crocodiles, and stuff themselves with rich clay soil as a special delicacy.

But to roast and devour little monkeys seemed to him the worst custom he had yet come across, and only out of devotion to his beloved science would he consent to have the roasted arm and hand of a monkey packed among their specimens to show to his learned friends in Paris.

As they continued their voyage in the tree-boat, Zerepe anxiously tapped the wood under their feet, saying, "Soon the crocodiles will be licking our soles." The bottom of the boat was wearing thin as, day in, day out, rocks, sharp-edged roots, and sand scraped and grated against it.

102

Aimé murmured gloomily, "The boat's draft is too great, we are overloaded."

There were eight monkeys looking excitedly through the bars of their cages: silky tamarins ruffling their yellow manes, and capuchins chattering through their teeth. In addition there were seven screeching parrots and parakeets, two pale green rockbirds that could fold and unfold their combs, a coati, a small armadillo, and a mad toucan with a grotesquely large beak who made the sign of the cross before taking a sip of water and had been nicknamed "God Bless."

At the next stop Alexander came out of the forest carrying on his arm a huge macaw whose crimson plumage shone in the sun like giant rubies.

"I hope you aren't planning to take him along!" protested Aimé.

"Why ever not?"

"Because we have no room."

"What—no room for one of these splendid birds who helped to discover America?" Alexander stepped into the boat with his parrot. In his tattered clothes, his face burned by the sun, Alexander looked for all the world like Robinson Crusoe.

"When Martín Alonzo Pinzón, who sailed with Columbus, saw a flight of parrots one evening flying in a southwesterly di-

rection," recounted Alexander, "he went to the Admiral and asked that the ships' course be changed. The idea had come to him forcibly, like an inspiration, and he owed it to the parrots. Rightly, he had surmised that the birds were making for land to find a resting place for the night. Never has a flight of birds had such far-reaching consequences. Following them, Columbus and those who sailed after him discovered the Bahamas, Cuba, and Haiti, and some years later the Spaniards

conquered the land of the Aztecs. What would have happened if Columbus had first stepped on North American soil? If he had landed, say, in Virginia or in the vicinity of New York? It can truthfully be said that the parrots were responsible for the way the European nations came to be distributed in the Americas."

Aimé had to admit that one could not refuse passage to a bird of such historic lineage, and the macaw was allowed on board.

Soon they had left the Casiquiare behind and had passed the famous confluence where the Orinoco divides into two arms, one of them, the Casiquiare, running south into the river basin of the Amazon. Alexander, with his two small titi monkeys rolled up in his lap, entered the exact course of these rivers on his charts.

Despite Zerepe's fears, the bottom of the tree-boat did not give way under them. They finally reached the rapids at Maipures, the spot from which, fifty days before, they had set out on their perilous voyage.

Zerepe became more and more excited as they drew near to the landing stage. When they entered the little bay he asked Alexander's permission to leave, and rushed off eagerly to the mission.

But in less than half an hour he was back, looking dejected and distraught.

"What's the matter?" asked Aimé, who was especially fond of him because Zerepe had helped him to collect many valuable plants.

"My sweetheart has run away," Zerepe blurted out.

"You'll find another," consoled Aimé, trying not to laugh at him.

But Zerepe shook his head. "Not one like her!" His grief was very great.

He had been born and baptized in the mission but had gone into the jungle to choose a bride, a girl with dark eyes and black hair and glittering white teeth that shone like the mica in the sand of the Orinoco. He had wanted to marry her, but then Alexander, needing an interpreter, had come between them. Although Alexander had promised that they would return to the mission, the other Indians had told the girl, "Zerepe won't come back; he has gone to the land of the Portuguese with the white men and they will keep him there." The girl waited for six weeks. Then she stole a canoe and with another girl made her way through the rapids and over the mountains back to her tribe.

"Don't take it to heart so," said Aimé. "You saw for yourself how many pretty girls there are in the jungle."

Zerepe sighed. "She was as supple as a snake and fiery as a black jaguar."

"Ah!" said Aimé, laughing. "I bet you thought she would work hard for you. Well, never mind, I haven't got a wife either."

This was poor consolation for Zerepe, who had dreamed of leading the life of a real Indian once he was married— hunting and fishing while his wife did all the work in the house.

Being a Christian, he could have only one wife. Other men of his tribe who lived in the jungle had two or three, but Zerepe looked down on them and thought them savages. They killed all twins, and children who were weak, or those on whom the demon-bird Tikitiki had put the evil eye; and sometimes they ate their enemies.

To these savages his sweetheart had returned. She had not waited for him. The Indians in the settlement had grinned contemptuously at him and had mocked him on his arrival. Hatred against the girl boiled up inside him. She had made him ridiculous, him—Zerepe—who understood the languages of all the tribes on the Orinoco, who collected plants for the white men and knew how to steer a boat through the river labyrinths.

Then he caught sight of Alexander feeding the monkeys near the boat. Was it not the white man who was responsible for all his misfortunes?

As long as he lived, the men of his tribe would make fun of the big strong man who caught himself a jaguar girl in the jungle and then couldn't keep her. To have been made a fool of by a woman was the worst possible disgrace in the eyes of the Indians, who thought of their women as their slaves.

Zerepe decided he must kill the white men—then no one would dare laugh at him. But he must kill them in such a way that their blood would not betray him.

"Aimé," Alexander called from the boat, "come along, we'll go bathing."

"Good idea! I'm longing to get into some clean clothes."

Alexander laughed. "I'll be digging the chiggers out of my poor feet. I'm bleeding like a stuck pig between the toes. Zerepe! See that we have something nice for supper."

"Yes, master."

Alexander and Aimé walked downstream until they came to a bar of rocks over which the water gushed and splashed in a whirl. They walked gingerly over the slippery boulders and bathed in the cool, clear pool that had formed at the upper edge of the bar. All around them thundered the waterfall, but there were no crocodiles, and even the mosquitoes were less troublesome than they had been in the swamps of the Casiquiare.

Meanwhile Zerepe supervised the setting up of the camp. In the middle went the leather trunk that contained the food and also served as a table. Next to it were put the instruments and the animal cages. Alexander's and Aimé's hammocks

107

were tied to trees, side by side, and underneath them the herbarium and specimen cases were stowed away. At the edge of the camp the Indian helpers spread out their mats, and near by they began piling up faggots for the nightly fire to keep the jaguars at bay.

Alexander's linen was kept in a trunk that also contained particularly valuable stones and plants. Right at the bottom of it were the test tubes with the curare.

Zerepe raised the top of the trunk to get a clean shirt and new socks for Alexander. As he took out the socks the idea struck him. Had he not heard Alexander speak of the open sores between his toes?

Zerepe looked around. The Indians were collecting firewood at the edge of the forest. The river was deserted. Quickly his hand slipped below the linen and dug down until it touched one of the glass tubes. He pulled it out and uncorked it.

A sharp crack close to his ears made him jump. But it was only the colorful manakin whose bearded throat could produce a roar of unprecedented proportions for its size. First the bird clicked its tongue with an explosive crack, then it screeched like a door on a rusty hinge, and finally came a deep rumbling roar that an angry bull could not have improved on. Even the oldest Indians felt a shiver run down their spines when they heard a manakin's rumble close by.

The curare had become semiliquid in the humid heat. Zerepe turned one of the socks inside out and smeared a little of the sticky paste on the tip of the toe.

The parrots screeched shrilly. As Zerepe turned around angrily the edge of the sock wiped against the glass tube.

The monkeys chattered behind the bars of their cages, threw back their heads, and stared at him with wide-open eyes and bared teeth.

The curare dripped into the trunk and onto the white linen.

108

Hastily, Zerepe recorked the tube and put it back, hid the soiled shirt underneath a clean one, turned the sock right side out, and threw it with its fellow on top of the linen, shutting the trunk with a snap.

"I am going to the mission," he called out to the other Indians. "Perhaps I can get a young pig to roast."

Alexander was limping when he returned with Aimé. He had dug out the chiggers from underneath his toenails and the open wounds burned like fire. The socks he wore were encrusted with blood.

He opened the trunk and took out the fresh pair that lay on top of the linen. Groaning, he leaned against the trunk, bent forward, and carefully drew on one sock. Then he took the second one and stretched it so that he could pull it more easily over his sore foot. The soft wool stuck to his thumb.

Alexander looked surprised. "Haven't you washed these socks?" he asked one of the Indians.

"Oh, yes, *Señor,* all clean," the man asserted.

Alexander shook his head. Well, a little glue wouldn't do any harm. The main thing was to get fresh socks on his feet. He bent down again to put his toes into the sock, but again it stuck to his thumb and suddenly—as if he had been struck by lightning—he knew what it must be.

He threw the sock onto the grass and dug feverishly into the trunk. One of the curare tubes was open! Part of the poison had oozed out onto a shirt and one of his notebooks.

Alexander took a deep breath. His pulse was racing, and he could feel how the blood had drained from his face. The inside of the sock was full of curare. If the edge had not been sticky he would have been a dead man within seconds.

Only one explanation seemed possible. The constant unloading of the trunk at each camp must have loosened the cork. Alexander's next thought was that he must warn future explorers of this danger and impress upon them the need for utmost vigilance when transporting curare or other poisons.

Zerepe returned from the mission with a year-old pig over his shoulder to find Alexander rinsing his socks and shirt in the river; this time he was not leaving the washing to the Indians.

Zerepe's first thought was to take flight, but then he heard Aimé exclaim, "What a miracle! What incredible luck!" and he stayed and listened.

"Stop talking about luck," Alexander said angrily. "If I hadn't taken the trouble to find out all that is known about curare I'd have put on that sock and no luck in the world could have prevented my dying."

"I don't know why you are so set against a bit of luck," replied Aimé in mock despair. "Wasn't it lucky that some of the stuff stuck to the edge of the sock?"

"How else could it have got inside?" was Alexander's irritated response. "What you call luck is nothing more nor less than what the Indians on the Orinoco call Cachimana, their good spirit, from whom they hope to get all they want, while the evil spirit, Jolokiamo, puts a spoke in their wheel; he can even open the white man's curare tubes. Let the Indians put their faith in spirits and demons. I'll stick to facts."

Zerepe listened spellbound. Although he had been brought up a Christian, he still believed firmly in the powerful spirits Cachimana and Jolokiamo. Too many times had he stood in the dark jungle listening to the sound of the sacred trumpets beseeching Cachimana to make the palm trees fruitful. And it made an unforgettable impression on him when he once saw a young girl being strangled by the elders of the tribe in punishment for having looked at one of these trumpets. All women, on pain of death, were forbidden to look upon these sacred instruments made of fired clay.

110

The spirits were mighty in the forest; there they held sway over life and death, even if the white men did not believe in their power. Zerepe knew better.

All the same, the white men were clever. They had discovered the poison in the sock and would most likely foil any other stratagem he might be able to think up.

When he heard Alexander speak contemptuously of the great spirit Jolokiamo, Zerepe had been horror-struck. But then a new idea came to him. What if he could deliver the white men into the power of the evil spirit of revenge? All he had to do was to induce them to commit some further outrage against Jolokiamo, then the spirit of his people would pursue the offenders wherever they went and would not rest until they were dead.

While he turned the spit on which the pig was being roasted, Zerepe considered his plan carefully, and when he took a piece of the juicy haunch to Alexander he knew exactly what he would do.

The Dead of Atoribe

"IN THE mountains behind the stream," Zerepe began, "there is a cave with many dead. A whole people lie buried there in baskets. No white men except the Fathers at the mission have ever seen them."

"Ah, you mean the skeletons in the cave at Atoribe which have caused so much trouble to Father Zea," replied Alexander.

"How can dead men cause trouble to a missionary?" Aimé wanted to know.

"He was seen visiting the cave, and the story was told around that he had been hiding a treasure among the skeletons. Of course, it's all nonsense, for Father Zea is as poor as the mission children he teaches, but the whole Orinoco territory lives in terror of the dead of Atoribe. It is said that they curse whoever disturbs their rest. Even the authorities in Angostura seem to be affected by this ridiculous superstition and take the view that anyone who goes to such an ill-omened place must have something to hide."

"Sounds like an interesting cave," said Aimé.

Zerepe eagerly seized his chance. "I know of a safe way to

112

get there," he put in. "We would only need to cross the first two waterfalls; after that it is not far."

Alexander eyed Zerepe with a searching look. "I thought all Indians were afraid of the cave," he said suspiciously.

"Only the wild Indians," lied Zerepe, cunningly.

"All right, if you will lead us, we can go tomorrow," decided Alexander.

Zerepe's eyes lit up with deadly hatred. He would deliver the two white men into the power of Jolokiamo like two flies caught in a spider's web. Then he, Zerepe, would stand by and watch as the spirit slowly killed them. He would taste the full flavor of revenge and yet no one could find blood on his hands.

That evening, when Alexander noted down the events of the day in his diary as usual, he did not forget about Zerepe's sweetheart, finishing his report with this mistakenly optimistic remark: "Zerepe's depression did not last long. He considers himself far above the people of his tribe. He won't find it difficult to forget a girl who grew up in the jungle."

Alexander had never been given to mistrusting people and even after the curare incident, which brought him within an inch of death, there was not the slightest flicker of suspicion in his mind.

Next morning the tree-boat, with its load of parrots and monkeys, slipped past green islands on its way downstream. The waterfalls roared and thundered as the little boat rocked and danced over the giant steps.

Zerepe steered toward a wall of granite rock, and the oarsmen pulled the boat onto the bank.

"Are we going to climb up there?" asked Aimé incredulously as he eyed the sheer drop of the rock face that rose black and forbidding out of the turbulent stream. Using the large quartz crystals jutting out of the cracks in the rock like nails for supports, they were able to climb up. Aimé was soon gasping for breath at this unaccustomed exercise. They paused in their perilous ascent on a narrow ledge, and Alexander, wiping his forehead with a handkerchief, remarked, "A scientist without strong muscles would be lost in a situation like this. Intelligence alone would be no good to him on this wall, unless he also had strong arms and legs, and plenty of guts and endurance."

When they reached the top of the mountain, a magnificent view spread out before them. Deep below lay hundreds of small islands in the giant river, and beyond the jungle the savanna stretched out unendingly to the distant horizon.

They walked in single file along a narrow trail to where the mountain sloped downward. Here rocks formed a gigantic vault over a deep cavern which, as Alexander pointed out, must have been washed out of the rock face by a tremendous tidal wave in prehistoric times. The tall, leafy forest grew right up to it from the valley below, and sweetly scented vanilla orchids and climbing begonias draped the entrance.

Zerepe and the other Indians waited outside while Alexander and Aimé went inside. Goatsuckers, flitting past like silent shadows, made them jump nervously. On the ground, arranged in neat rows, they saw hundreds of square baskets, finely woven from the stalks of palm fronds. They counted the rows and calculated that there were over six hundred baskets, some small, some large.

Inside the baskets, in doubled-up positions, lay well-preserved, complete skeletons with not a rib, not as much as the joint of a finger missing. The bones were coated with a kind of red paint. Besides the skeletons there were also mummies preserved in a covering of banana leaves and strong-scented pitch.

Between the baskets stood tall urns of gray-blue clay with

handles in the shape of crocodiles and snakes. In these urns whole families seemed to have been interred.

Most of the dead had been there for only a little over a hundred years. They were the last remains of the great war-like tribe of the Atorais, who, pursued by the Caribs, withdrew to this isolated rock fastness and gradually died out. Now nothing was left to tell of that once mighty Indian nation except this silent vault and an incredibly ancient parrot that could say many words that no one understood because, so the Indians believed, they were Atorai words.

Alexander took several skulls out of the baskets and carried them outside to have a better look at them.

An evil smile curled Zerepe's lips when he saw Alexander with the skulls, but the other Indians shouted, "Put them back or you will be a dead man!" and ran off in terror along the way they had come, exclaiming all the while, "The spirit of the dead will take vengeance!"

Alexander, paying not the slightest attention to these warnings, took a good look at the skulls. All except two were typical Indian heads, and the two that were differently shaped probably belonged to mestizos—half-breeds—who married Atorai women and remained with their wives' people.

"Zerepe, we'll take a few of the baskets back with us. Lend me a hand."

Zerepe stood stock-still as if nailed to the ground. His grin had vanished and, instead, his face was transfixed with horror. What Alexander wanted him to do would mean his own death too.

"No, master, this would bring disaster!"

"But I thought you weren't afraid. Aren't you a Christian?"

"No one may touch them—not even a Christian," stammered Zerepe.

"Get along with you," said Alexander impatiently. "It is

important that at least a few skeletons of this extinct race should be preserved."

"No, no, no!" Zerepe took to his heels and fled after his fellow tribesmen.

So Alexander and Aimé had to carry the baskets themselves. They took several skulls, the skeleton of a child about seven years old, and two adult skeletons, and began the difficult return trip.

Dusk had fallen. Swarms of insects hovered like pink clouds of mist over the mountain slopes, and the ground, overgrown with dense vegetation, seemed on fire with glowworms.

While they walked, Alexander reflected: Whole nations

pass away and flowering civilizations wither and turn to dust. But new life springs up eternally, and ceaselessly nature renews itself in a fresh blossoming, unconcerned by what man, with his futile quarrels and dissensions, will do to the ripening fruit.

No Indian was to be seen when they got back to the boat. "Quickly," said Alexander, "we'll wrap mats around the baskets so that no one will know what they contain. Otherwise these madly superstitious Indians are quite capable of leaving us to continue our journey to Angostura alone."

But Alexander sought them out and attempted to convince them that they could safely travel in the boat since it was only he and Aimé who had taken the skulls out of the vault.

"The dead will call on the crocodiles to make the boat sink in midstream," the Indians predicted angrily.

"If they are really as powerful as you say," replied Alexander, "they will be just, too, and punish only the guilty. The crocodiles will be told to devour only me and my white brother. You can't be held responsible for what we did."

The argument went to and fro half the night, but in the morning the Indians launched the boat and carried the bird and monkey cages on board while Alexander and Aimé stowed away the skeleton baskets, wrapped in the innocent-looking mats, among the chests of the herbarium.

When they were ready to push off, Zerepe had disappeared. It was clear that he had fled in fear of the dead men's curses. The other Indians were beginning to waver again; but Alexander saved the situation with a joke: "You don't want to run after a lovesick fool who's gone to look for his sweetheart in the jungle!"

They laughed. "Zerepe isn't man enough to handle a boat," they said. "He's just a fool."

They pushed the oars into the tumbling waves and took the boat out into the middle of the wide river. An old Indian with a weather-worn face held the tiller.

Alexander was anxious to leave the vicinity of Atoribe as quickly as possible. It would not have surprised him if Zerepe tried to stir up the wild tribes along the riverbank to whom the big vault on the mountain was a sacred shrine.

"Can you take us over the rapids?" he asked the man at the helm.

The old man ran his eyes over the boat with its load of cages, trunks, chests, and baskets, looked thoughtfully at the thin bottom through which the water had begun to seep, and then gazed fixedly at Alexander as if he wondered why the white man was in such a hurry all of a sudden. Finally he nodded casually. It wasn't his boat, and it was all the same to him if the white men wanted to break their necks in the rapids.

And so, carried on by the swift current, they raced toward the thundering rapids. When they were right in the middle of the seething turmoil, a tropical thunderstorm broke over their heads. Rain came down in torrents and lightning flashed all around. The little monkeys screamed in their cages, and the huge heads of ancient crocodiles emerged from the deep, close to the trembling, fragile craft.

It was a journey for life or death. Aimé thought of the dead men who were their shipmates, and a cold shiver ran down his spine despite the sweltering heat. When a flash of lightning lit up the steersman's face, he thought he saw Death himself sitting at the rudder. Then he realized that he had a fever and took his pulse. It was over ninety!

By nightfall they had left the rapids behind. The thunderstorm had passed and their little boat was bounding downstream under a clear, starry sky.

Aimé paid little attention to his attack of fever. Next day, he busied himself looking for specimens near the mouth of one of the tributaries of the Orinoco. Afterward, in the middle of a cloudburst, he dissected a large sea cow. Meanwhile Alexander carried on with his surveying work and filled his notebooks with more figures. He measured the river and took the temperature of the water.

And so, pursued by swarms of mosquitoes that feasted on their blood day and night, they arrived on the seventy-fifth day of their adventurous river voyage in the harbor of Angostura, now Bolívar, in Venezuela.

The Governor of Guiana Province gave them quarters in his house, and after they had discharged the Indians they sank exhausted into their beds. It was their first night's rest in six weeks without lurking danger from crocodiles, snakes, and jaguars.

Still, Aimé awoke with chattering teeth. He had a high temperature and kept raving about the dead of Atoribe. Was their curse to prove effective after all? Alexander blamed himself bitterly. It had been his wish that they should undertake the Orinoco trip instead of remaining in the more temperate climate of the Sierra Nevada, and he felt it would be his fault entirely if Aimé now fell a victim to malaria.

As Aimé's condition grew rapidly worse, Alexander did not move from his bedside.

"If I die," the sick man whispered, "write to my mother, Kies!" Neither of them noticed that he was using his friend's old nickname, about which Alexander had once told him when they were exchanging childhood reminiscences.

"You are not going to die," said Alexander. "Remember, you've always had luck."

Aimé made a despairing gesture with his hand. "How often we have quarreled about luck and knowledge—which of the two it is better to put your faith in. You would never have anything to do with luck. Now I would give a lot if, as a doctor, I knew a little more about this treacherous fever and had something besides luck to aid me," he groaned through parched lips.

"One day medical science will find out where the fever comes from," replied Alexander reassuringly and gave him a tincture of china bark which Aimé had himself collected.

Not until almost a hundred years later did the English physician Sir Ronald Ross, in India, and the Italian zoologist Grassi, in Rome, discover that the Anopheles mosquito transmits the malaria germ to human beings. They were both awarded the Nobel Prize for their discovery. Before then, the bad air in the swamps was thought to be responsible for the disease, and this explains its name, *mal* meaning bad, and *aria* air.

For a long time china (or Peruvian) bark was the only known remedy. This was accidentally discovered by a fever-stricken Spanish soldier who was cured after drinking from a puddle into which a twig from a cinchona tree had fallen. The name *china* may come from the Indian word for bark, *kina*, or from the cinchona tree which was named after one of the viceroys of Peru, a Count Chinchón. The quinine of modern times comes from the same bark.

Alexander made a careful study of malaria, but he never found out what caused it or how it was transmitted. He fell ill with it, too, but after dosing himself with strong tinctures of china bark and honey he was spared further attacks.

Aimé, who had contracted dysentery as well as malaria, prescribed herbal remedies for himself which Alexander dispensed, nursing him devotedly day and night. For weeks Aimé hovered between life and death, but together they beat the disease, and he began to get better.

Then his first thought was for the safety of his beloved

herbarium. "We must get back to Cumaná," he insisted. "If we stay here much longer everything will be ruined. I won't have a moment's peace until we have sent our collections back to Europe."

"I have looked through your herbarium," replied Alexander. "Do you know how many samples of plants you have classified?"

Aimé shook his head. Figures had never been his strong point.

"Including duplicates, you have twelve thousand specimens, and thirty-five hundred of them belong to species hitherto unknown to botanical science. Do you know what this means?"

Aimé shrugged his shoulders. "If it hadn't been for the ants and the mildew, I'd have three times as many."

"My dear man, up to the middle of this century only about three thousand species of plants had been classified. With your work you'll become known as one of the foremost botanists in the world."

"Ah—now I know why you have been nursing me so well. You want to share in my triumphal entry into Paris!"

"That's about it," said Alexander, laughing. "Now, let's ride back to Cumaná across the savanna."

A long train of mules laden with the chests and trunks threaded its way across the silent plain, which seemed to undulate like an ocean wave in the heat haze. The monkeys, perched on top of the packs, tried to snatch the red conelike fruits of the mauritia palms whenever the mules passed under one of those trees.

On the third day they halted at an Indian mission settlement in the middle of the endless savanna. The women who crowded around the mule train and teased the monkeys wore no clothes, but the men had lengths of royal blue cloth draped around their thighs. Their athletic bodies were painted with

121

a red dye and with their picturesque drapings they reminded Alexander of antique statues.

When the women saw the pine needles that Aimé used to secure his plants on the paper before pressing, they begged for them with raised hands.

Generously, Aimé distributed the needles, but since these ladies had no pockets in their bright red paint, they used their underlip as a needle-holder. Pulling the lip down with one hand, they pushed the needles right through with the other, so that the heads stayed on the inside and the pointed ends stuck out in a neat row on the outside.

During the next few hours the tip of Aimé's tongue repeatedly felt cautiously along the inner edge of his lip, and he winced at the thought that it might be studded with a row of needles.

The next morning he was confronted with an even more serious matter. Alexander had got up first and was evidently involved in a violent argument with the drivers of the mule train. Out of the confused shouts and yells, Aimé discovered to his consternation that the Indians had found out about the skeletons from the Atoribe vault.

Alexander tried to make out that the baskets wrapped in mats contained the bones of sea cows and the skins of crocodiles, but the men did not believe him. "We can smell the pitch with which the dead of Atoribe were embalmed," they shouted.

Finally, Aimé had to call one of the monks from the mission to bring the Indians to their senses. "Our dead kinsmen won't go to your land," they prophesied grimly as the mule train started off again.

It took thirteen days to cross the flat and desolate savanna. Alexander found himself wondering if it might not be possible to irrigate this vast wasteland close to the equator with wells and canals and to plant trees and bushes.

"I feel sure that a large part of this plain will one day be turned into fertile land by an energetic government," he said.

"Ever since the Europeans first came to this country," replied Aimé thoughtfully, "they have had only one aim, and that was to get rich as quickly and comfortably as they could. Why do you think the vault at Atoribe was untouched? Because there was nothing valuable there and none of the white settlers was interested in the history and origin of the Indian races. They'd be just as uninterested in wells and canals and in tree plantations."

"But gold deposits are soon exhausted," replied Alexander. "In the sixteenth century the Spaniards collected fabulous fortunes in gold by ransacking graves in Peru, and now the burial places of that ancient civilization are destroyed. I can't help thinking that one day the plow will turn these vast stretches of wilderness into arable land, and a new civilization will be born."

"It would be a wonderful opportunity for a botanist to settle down here and experiment with different crops," mused Aimé. The more he thought about it the more enthusiastic he became, and in imagination he conjured up whole plantations of orange and lemon groves, banana plants and tea shrubs, strawberry beds, and forests of various kinds of palms all grown from carefully chosen seedlings. As he became absorbed in these new ideas he shook off the last traces of weariness left behind by the malaria, and by the time the mule train reached Barcelona on the north coast of Venezuela Aimé was as fit as ever.

From Barcelona it was not far to Cumaná. They began to count the hours until their collections could be stowed away

123

on a Spanish mail boat and be safely on their way to Europe.
But fate willed otherwise.

On the day they arrived in Barcelona, Alexander contracted typhoid fever, and any thought of continuing the journey had to be abandoned. He had hardly recovered when, during his first outing to the hot sulfur springs at the edge of the
mountains, his horse—an exceptionally fine animal—was torn

from him by crocodiles in the river Naricual. Now even Alexander began to feel uneasy. A sense of foreboding took hold of him as he thought anxiously of their priceless collection of specimens. Not a day longer would he loiter in Barcelona.

They rented space on an open boat bound for Cumaná with a cargo of cacao and took their cases and chests as well as the birds and monkeys aboard.

By evening they were heading out to sea in beautiful weather.

"I had begun to think that the dead of Atoribe had really put a curse on us," said Aimé, with a sidelong glance at the baskets filled with skulls and other bones.

Christopher Columbus

"A SCIENTIST is like a soldier in battle," mused Alexander as the cacao boat left the mouth of the Rio Neveri. "He must be prepared to stay behind on the field, and that's why he is wise if he sees to it that the results of his work are brought to safety in good time."

Hardly were the words out of his mouth when a two-master rounded the cliffs of the island of Borracha and headed toward them, her sails billowing. Bursts of musket shots exploded in the air, and the bullets hit the water to the right and left of their small boat.

"Pirates! We are lost!" exclaimed the terrified boatman as he tore down the sail from his mast.

A dinghy came alongside and soldiers, with muskets at the ready, jumped aboard.

"What have you got in your cases and those baskets?" they shouted at the boatman, ignoring Alexander's protests.

Then they found the sacks of cacao. "Smugglers! Your cargo is confiscated and you come with us."

The muskets pointed at Alexander, and, fuming with rage, both he and Aimé were taken across to the two-master. The captain of the privateer listened to Alexander's indignant protests with a condescending smile.

"If you are scientists as you say, perhaps you can explain to me what you are doing with a load of cacao?" he said sarcastically. "It is my duty to arrest you and take you and your cargo to Canada."

"To Canada!" Alexander pushed his and Aimé's Spanish passports under the captain's nose, but to no avail.

"Strange that you as a German should be traveling under the protection of the Spanish government. This makes you doubly suspicious."

Now Alexander lost all control over himself and began to rave at the captain: "This intolerance against the search for knowledge and against liberty of thought is the most despicable of all forms of persecution. And equally despicable are petty tyrants dressed up as politicians and bigoted hypocrites who babble about 'their duty' when they are out for nothing but revenge."

Aimé went white to the gills during this outburst. The captain was not the man to tolerate this sort of language. At any moment he might have them put in chains, and they would not see the light of day again, until they arrived in Canada or goodness knows where. Meanwhile their collections would molder and rot. Again Aimé thought of the curse of the dead men as the captain's hand gripped the pistol that lay before him. "So, you are going to be troublesome," he said in an ominous voice. "I am sorry for you."

Then he paused and listened to a sudden commotion up on deck. A sailor burst into the cabin and whispered excitedly into the captain's ear, while a cannon shot rang out across the sea.

The captain eyed Alexander fiercely. "You will wait here until I return," he said, and disappeared up the gangway.

A quarter of an hour later he came back with an officer of the British navy. The English frigate *Hawk* had intercepted

127

the privateer, and the prisoners, together with the Venezuelan boat, were handed into the custody of the British officer. Alexander and Aimé made one more trip in a rowboat—this time to the English man-of-war.

"I am no longer surprised at anything," declared Aimé. "At least things can't turn out much worse than with those filthy pirates."

On board the frigate her captain introduced himself as John Garnier and wanted to know if Alexander was the naturalist von Humboldt he had heard about. Alexander acknowledged that he was, and asked in his turn, "Are you the Captain Garnier who accompanied George Vancouver on his voyage of discovery to the North Pacific?"

"That's me," said the captain, laughing, and they shook hands like old comrades who had fought on separate fronts in the same great battle for the discovery of the unknown.

It wasn't long before they were all sitting down together with whisky and cigars, absorbed in the conversation of men who have weathered all kinds of dangers in far-off corners of the earth, and exchanging tales of their experiences. As a farewell present Captain Garnier gave Alexander some mathematical calculation tables on the positions of the planets, which helped him greatly in his astronomical work.

Instead of being carted off to Canada, they sailed away in the early dawn toward Cumaná in the cacao boat. The parrots flapped their wings and the monkeys clapped their hands.

After these experiences Alexander was even less inclined to leave anything to chance. As soon as they arrived in hospitable Cumaná, where a villa was put at their disposal, he began to divide Aimé's herbarium. "At a time when privateers roam the sea, and neutral passports offer as little protection as neutral ships, we must distribute our collections on as many separate transports as possible."

128

Aimé protested, "I don't understand you. You are pulling my work to pieces. Everything has gone well so far. . . ."

"You had better make copies of your two volumes of plant descriptions and classifications."

"What?" Aimé couldn't believe his ears. "Copy out all those thousands of systematic descriptions? But our friend Friar Gonzales has promised to take all of our cases safely to Europe. Don't you think him trustworthy?"

"When will you stop relying on other people, Aimé? Of course the friar is trustworthy, but what about the hazards of the sea?"

"Anything that may happen to the mail packet on which Gonzales travels can happen to every other ship."

"Yes, but four ships are safer than one, my scientific friend! Listen—we'll send the parrots, the manakins, the toucans, and the monkeys on a French ship of the line. If she is attacked by the English fleet and lost, we still have all our other collections, the plants, the insects, the minerals, and our notebooks. If you can manage to copy your plant descriptions, we'll send one copy with Gonzales and keep the other here."

"Pessimist," grumbled Aimé as he sharpened the quill of a pink flamingo feather and looked despairingly at the high pile of papers, the work of many months, and began writing.

The birds and monkeys were sent aboard the French ship, but they all succumbed within a short time to the rigors of the climate, and not one specimen of the colorful menagerie reached Paris alive.

Aimé wrote day and night. When he had finally finished, Friar Gonzales arrived with the news that the English fleet had tightened its blockade and that there was now no chance of being able to leave for Spain from a South American port.

"I shall try to reach Cuba," he said. "I am told ships are still sailing for Spain from the harbor of Havana."

129

"Off to Cuba!" exclaimed Alexander, who was fretting impatiently at the long delay.

And so, on a cool November night in the year 1800, they once more set out to sea with all their baggage. The Franciscan friar sailed with them. Their boat was a North American freighter carrying salt meat, which stank to high heaven. There was no sign of the friendly English frigate, nor of the privateer, as they sailed out of Cumaná past the island of Borracha; instead they ran into a storm that whipped up mountainous waves and clouds of spray. The freighter pitched and tossed, with her sails filled to bursting. Her tackle creaked and groaned under the lash of the wind as if at any moment it were going to topple overboard together with the perilously slanting mast.

Then a voice yelled, "Fire!" Crackling flames began to lick the upper deck where red-hot coals had fallen out of the galley stove. One spark in the hold where the fat cattle from the llanos were and the whole ship would go up in flames like a torch. Fat meat burns almost as readily as oil.

Luckily, a huge wave washed overboard at the right moment and the fire was brought under control.

But the storm raged on. Amidst tropical rains, a sudden squall from north-northwest drove the freighter toward the white-crested line of breakers that broke over treacherous reefs. Only at the last moment was the captain able to turn about and avoid shipwreck. For twenty-five days the ship battled against sea and reefs, and the meat in the hold filled the air with such a stench that even the oldest sailors subsisted on nothing but rum and tobacco. But Alexander, oblivious to his surroundings, spent the time taking soundings and temperature readings, and tilted his sextant at the moon whenever it showed itself.

A few days after their arrival in Havana a Spanish packet left for Cádiz, in Spain, with all their specimen cases, including the skeleton baskets. The friar put the copy of Aimé's plant descriptions in his leather portfolio.

"Look after our treasures well," pleaded Alexander. "They are the fruits of more than a year's hard labor."

"You have seen for yourself, Father, that these tales about the curse of the dead of Atoribe are mere talk," added Aimé jokingly. They laughed and shook hands. At this moment the ship's bell began to ring.

A cold shiver ran down Alexander's spine. When was it that he had last heard the sound of a tolling ship's bell? Then he remembered; it had been on the *Pizarro* when the bell announced the death of a sailor.

Slowly the packet boat slid out of the deep, clover-shaped bay of Havana toward the open sea. It never reached Cádiz. Nothing was ever seen or heard again of the Franciscan friar and the priceless collection in his charge. Somewhere at the bottom of the sea between America and Africa lie the ship and, buried in it, all the butterflies, the plants, the minerals —and the bones of the Atoribe skeletons.

The drivers of the mule train had been right. Their dead kinsmen did not go to the white man's country.

After much thought Alexander had decided at the last moment not to entrust his notebooks and journals to Father Gonzales, and so, thanks to his inborn reluctance to trust to chance, he saved at least these quite irreplaceable documents which give his own account of his explorations in Venezuela.

When the ship had left, the two friends returned silently to the town. They felt as if a door had shut behind them; a chapter in their lives which began so long ago in the Rue du Vieux-Colombier in Paris had come to a close.

Before them rose in simple, solemn dignity the west front of Havana Cathedral. Could there be a better ending to the long months of struggle and hardship, of achievements and disappointments in discovery, than a visit to the tomb of the man who was the first European to set foot on this continent which they had labored to explore?

Aimé pushed against the heavy portal of the cathedral. The sound of their footsteps on the stone flagging echoed from the roof, and the flickering light of candles cast shadows on the towering walls of the nave. They stopped before a white stone on which in the fading twilight they read the name *Cristoforo Colombo*.

Aimé walked slowly around the tomb and touched a withered wreath that lay on the stone lid. Underneath it, then, lay the man who, as Admiral, had sailed to a new world, and beside him in his lead coffin lay also the iron chains in which he was transported back to Europe like a criminal on his third voyage.

As if he could read the thoughts that were passing through

132

Aimé's mind, Alexander said quietly, "Whatever adventures and experiences, successes or failures, still lie before us, you can see them all summed up here in the life story of this one man at your feet. He went in purple, and in chains; he was hailed as the greatest man on earth, yet was also vilified and condemned. Though the world had honored him, he died a forgotten man. But neither his triumph nor his downfall really matters. Only deeds count, and what he did will remain for all time our challenge and example."

They turned and went outside. Gusts of a southwesterly wind blew like a fanfare of trumpets through the streets, while the slender palms swayed gracefully to and fro like dancers. And from afar came the melancholy sound of slaves singing their haunting songs in the Negro quarter of Havana.

To the Heights of the Andes

THE icy dome of Chimborazo, covered in eternal snows, sparkled in the blinding sun of that June day in the year 1802. No man had ever conquered this mighty mountain with its five summits whose glaciers reached down into the deep valleys.

In a house in Riobamba, Aimé was bandaging Alexander's foot. "You cannot possibly climb rocks with your feet in this state," he said. "I have never seen anything like it. You are walking on raw flesh."

Alexander frowned. "I have managed so far. We got to the top of Pichincha, near Quito, at the third try, remember? We've climbed the volcano Antisana and paid our visit to Cotopaxi, the highest active volcano on earth. Don't ask me to turn back now."

"But Chimborazo is much higher than all those others," interrupted Aimé as he put a linen dressing between Alexander's toes.

"That's exactly why we must get to the top of it. We'll be the first with enough courage to succeed."

"I don't doubt the courage," replied Aimé dryly, wrapping the gauze around his patient's foot. "It's your feet I have my doubts about."

134

Alexander's sores dated back to their voyage on the Orinoco when he had been digging the chiggers out of his skin with blunt nails. Just when the deep holes in his flesh were beginning to heal, he had wandered about ankle-deep in the fine pumice dust of the Llano de Tapia, carrying out surveying work. The dust had settled between his toes and rubbed open the old wounds, but despite burning pains and the deadly danger of blood poisoning he had gone on until his work was finished.

"During the last few weeks you have come close to death more than once," Aimé reminded him. "On Pichincha, at

our first ascent, you fainted close to a red-hot lava pool, at a height of twelve thousand feet. During the second ascent you would have toppled over an overhanging crag into the open crater . . ."

"If the flickering flames from down below had not warned me in time," finished Alexander. "Why worry over past dangers? The main thing is not to have wasted your life on idle pursuits."

While he talked, he was putting on his new boots, made for him by an Indian shoemaker in Quito from llama skins. Although the leather was soft and supple, pulling on the boot still felt as if red-hot nails were being driven into his feet. Alexander talked loudly and rapidly to dull the pain. When he got up he turned to the window so that Aimé should not see him wince.

"*Señores*—the mules are saddled. What are we waiting

136

for?" a clear voice called from the courtyard below. This was young Carlos, the brother of a high Spanish official in the province of Quito, who had joined Alexander and Aimé on all their earlier mountain climbs in the Cordillera. Alexander was a man after Carlos' own heart, in which the adventurous spirit of the conquistadors still burned brightly, not yet spoiled by idleness and too much wealth. Now he was panting to take part in their assault on Chimborazo.

Since the Himalayas and the giant summits of the Peruvian Cordillera were still unknown at the time, the 20,577-foot-high Chimborazo was considered to be the highest mountain in the world.

"We are coming," Alexander called back, and turning to Aimé he said, "Bring your luck along. We may need it!"

Aimé grabbed his specimen box, Alexander the instrument bag in which he kept his barometer and thermometer, and together they rushed downstairs to mount the mules with the aid of wooden shoes that hung down from the saddle in place of stirrups.

Looking like a little band of scurrying ants in the shadow of the mighty mountain, the column of riders—three white men, one mestizo, and four Indians—made its way across the sandfields of Riobamba and followed the course of the Chibunga River. The upland plain was dotted with round lava hillocks on which cacti had established themselves, and thousands of llamas in their gleaming woolen coats were grazing on the olive-green pastures, keeping a wary eye on the riders.

Vultures, with a wing span of twelve feet or more, were circling along the steep wall of towering rocks ahead, searching for game that might have got trapped in the gullies and crevasses.

A brooding melancholy lay over the plain, which stretched

along the foot of the mountain range. "Even the desert was not as depressing as this lonely, silent place," remarked Aimé. "Now I know why llamas have such sad eyes."

They spent the night at an Indian village in the foothills, and next morning, before sunrise, they rode along terraces formed by ancient, hardened lava up to the line of the eternal snow. Here, petrified lava streams coiled in bulging spirals on the stony ground, a reminder of the days when the Chimborazo was a fire-spewing monster.

They left the mules behind near the last forsaken mountain huts and began the ascent.

New snow had fallen during the night and lay in a thin cover over the sharp-edged stony rubble, which cut into the thin soles of Alexander's shoes and dug into the wounds on his toes.

When the towering wall of rocks, in part fissured and corroded into giant pillars, barred their way, they made a detour and reached a narrow ridge shrouded in mountain mist.

At this spot the Indians refused to go any farther. "We can't breathe; we'll slip and fall," they panted.

Carlos cursed them, but Alexander began to plead with them even though he knew it would do no good. "You can't leave us here—you are carrying our food and water."

But the Indians shook their heads. "The mountain doesn't want to be climbed. For many days it shone brightly in the sun. Today it has hidden itself behind clouds. It has made the snow fall so that we should lose our way, and now it has stopped our throats so that we can't breathe."

Again Alexander tried to reason with them. If the bearers turned back, the rest of their party would be completely at the mercy of the weather. Should the mist not lift and they got lost among the rocks, there would be no hope of survival without provisions.

138

While Alexander was arguing with the Indians, the mountain seemed to be determined to show them what perils and dangers they were facing. The mist parted for a few seconds. On their left the rock face sloped down steeply into a bottomless pit, its surface covered with frozen snow, smooth as a sheet of glass. One false step, and a man would slide down the icy slope into the abyss. On their right, sheer cliffs dropped down vertically with not so much as a fleck of snow on them, while weathered crags and pinnacles stabbed through the clouds like hostile sentinels.

At this sight the Indians turned and fled, but not the mestizo. "Miserable cowards!" he called after them, and with a questioning look at Alexander he tapped his elbow against the basket he carried strapped on his back. "I have enough food and drink for today, *Señor*," he said.

"You will stay with us?"

"Yes, *Señor*, I am not afraid!"

"Then we will go on."

The mist had closed in again and there was not a breath of wind. The ice crunched under their feet, but around the seams of their boots the snow melted and the leather soaked up the water like a sponge. Soon Alexander's socks and bandages were wet through.

The ridge grew narrower until finally it was hardly as wide as the seat of an ordinary chair. They held their bodies slanted to the right as they walked since it seemed more dangerous to slip down the icy slope on the left than to fall on the side of the vertical drop which was hidden from view by the dense mist.

Like blind men they groped their way forward and upward on their hands and knees. The sharp-edged stones cut into their frozen hands and the breath from their mouths merged with the white, drifting mist.

Alexander began to feel dizzy. There was a drumming in his ears and the blood throbbed in his temples like hammer blows on an anvil. The mountain sickness, caused by the reduced oxygen content of the air at high altitudes, rendered him almost insensible. His limbs felt numb and as heavy as lumps of lead. Bending over double, he tried to breathe in deeply. His mouth and throat were so parched that when he swallowed he nearly screamed with pain. But when he had recovered a little, he forced himself to go on with dogged determination.

Meanwhile a thin trickle of blood was seeping out of the corners of Carlos' mouth and freezing on his chin. In the low atmospheric pressure his gums had begun to bleed.

We've got to turn back, thought Alexander, wiping his burning eyes with the back of his hand. Turn back and try again in better weather. But the very thought galled him. I was going to be the first man ever to attempt this climb. If only I did not feel so wretchedly ill, his soundless monologue continued. I can hardly keep my head up and red spots are dancing in front of my eyes. Maybe I have blood all over them. It might have been better to wait until my feet were properly healed.

He made an effort to swallow so as to keep down the thumping in his eardrums. There was nothing to be seen but the ice-covered stony ridge and the mist. The eerie silence all around weighed on his mind, and for a moment it seemed to him as if he were no longer on the earth but was stumbling about on some unknown star.

Nonsense, he admonished himself. If I wait until the wounds on my feet are healed I'll never get to the top of this mountain. Everyone has his sore and weak spots; the thing to do is to ignore them if you want to get anywhere.

The mist shifted up and down, although there was not the

faintest breath of wind. Alexander had never experienced such complete calm on a high mountain before. The air seemed benumbed and torpid as if the mountain itself were holding its breath.

How high were they? Alexander would have liked to take his altimeter out of his instrument bag but he feared to lose too much time in setting it up and so decided against it.

It was Aimé who suddenly shouted out, "Here it is!" His voice was hoarse and croaking and he choked with a convulsive fit of coughing.

Alexander stopped and stared. Slowly the pearl-gray curtain of mist parted as if drawn aside by invisible hands, and there immediately in front of his eyes rose the silvery dome of Chimborazo, brilliantly white against a royal-blue sky.

It was a wonderful sight. The mountaineers drew together and looked up at it in silent rapture.

They were bleeding at the mouth, their hands were torn and their feet numb and wet. The thin air made their hearts race as in a fever and they were fighting for breath with gaping mouths; their tongues were swollen and their legs felt too weak to carry them, but their eyes shone with the wonder before them.

"Let's go," said Alexander, and climbed on.

The sight of the summit almost within reach of their hands had given them new strength. They pushed on up the rocky ridge with short, rapid steps, their dizzy heads wobbling from side to side and down upon their chests.

The ledge broadened and then led in a gently rising curve straight to the foot of dark, massive rocks over which the steeply rising glaciers, cleft and torn by ravines, stretched their white tentacles; above them towered the majestic summit like a throne.

The ridge continued in a bold sweep halfway up the rock

face, where it stopped abruptly and a sheer stone wall sank vertically into a deep shaft. Startled, Alexander took a step back while Carlos threw himself on the ground and peered over the edge. "It goes down for nearly four hundred yards," he said.

Aimé groped along the rock face. "We must try to get across the gully," he gasped.

"It's more than sixty feet wide," whispered Alexander, who had lost his voice, partly from exhaustion and the altitude and partly from excitement.

Together they tried to find a way of climbing across the chasm, but there was not a single foothold. "It's as if the god of the Incas had split the mountain with an ax," murmured Carlos.

It was now one o'clock in the afternoon. Alexander carefully set up his altimeter while Aimé took the temperature. The mercury showed 27° F., which, after the tropical heat of the Venezuelan jungle, seemed like the North Pole to them. Meanwhile Alexander calculated the height they had reached —it was 18,600 feet.

"This is the highest point ever reached by man," exclaimed the astonished Aimé.

"It's less than two thousand feet to the top," added Carlos, and they all looked up longingly, but the summit was again shrouded in mist.

Even though they had not reached their final goal, they felt very proud of their achievement. No one before them had ever climbed this titan of ice and snow to such a height. They were the first mountaineers to challenge this giant among the South American volcanoes on the equator, and they did it without the modern aids and equipment available to later climbers.

The sky had clouded over and Alexander was anxious to start the descent. It looked like more snow and every minute of delay spelled growing danger.

The mestizo was in a bad way and could barely drag himself along. Violent coughing fits shook his body, which was trembling all over with the cold.

Cautiously, they followed the narrow ridge down, groping their way through the thickening mist. The lower they got the more intense became the sense of foreboding which drove them on. Like animals scenting danger, they fled, convinced that something terrible was about to happen.

The milky-white mist darkened to a steely gray and then turned into a yellow fog. They panted and choked, their thumping hearts near to bursting, but they dared not take a moment's rest. The trickiest part of the descent was hardly behind them when a furious hailstorm broke over their heads. The ice came hurtling into their faces and they pulled their jackets over their heads for protection. Had the storm overtaken them a few minutes earlier it would have swept them off the ridge down into the abyss.

It grew even darker, and when the hailstorm stopped a thick blanket of snow descended silently from a black sky. Alexander's eyes were burning like fire. Staring fixedly at the path ahead, he saw it vanish from sight under the white snow.

They summoned up their last reserve of strength and trudged on while the crunching snow under their feet piled up higher and higher.

At last they arrived back at the mountain huts where they had spent the previous night, and collapsed into their bunks.

In the following century four attempts to climb Chimborazo from the north, east, and south sides failed, and it was not until 1880 that the English mountaineer Edward Whymper with

144

two Swiss guides conquered the mighty giant, reaching the summit from the southwest.

When Aimé woke up next morning, the sun was peeping into the wooden hut through the slats, and specks of hay dust flittered in the light beams. At first he could not remember where he was. Every bone in his body ached, he had a splitting headache, and his throat burned as if he had been drinking pure acid. Groaning, he raised himself and looked about. In the corner Carlos was fast asleep with the snoring mestizo by his side. Alexander was sitting outside in the sun, writing in his notebook. Chimborazo, without so much as a wisp of cloud, was smiling down at him.

"Had a good sleep?" Alexander asked as Aimé's tousled head appeared in the doorway.

"No, I'm as stiff as a post."

"What you need is some good exercise. Come and have your breakfast. In half an hour we'll be on our way."

"What?" croaked Aimé, putting his hand to his rasping throat. "Haven't you got any pains?"

"Yes, but I don't bother to think about them."

"I can't do that," replied Aimé fretfully. "I have only to lift a knee and the pain shoots right through me."

Alexander laughed and poured him a cup of maté tea. "Just imagine," he said, nodding his head toward Chimborazo, "the old colossus suddenly coming to life again, spitting molten fire and rocks. Many a volcano was thought to be dead and then, all of a sudden . . ."

Aimé considered this while he drank his tea. "It'd be like the end of the world," he whispered. "The whole province would be buried under lava."

145

"And you would run for your life, pains or no pains," concluded Alexander in a matter-of-fact tone.

"Right as usual," conceded Aimé. Then he hammered on the wall of the hut to wake Carlos and the mestizo, washed himself in the ice-cold water of a mountain spring, and fell hungrily on his breakfast.

Alexander was studying the map. "Are you looking for a new mountain?" asked Aimé suspiciously.

"No, but yesterday on Chimborazo, Carlos mentioned the Incas. We might go to see what we can still find of their legendary realm."

"Then we should go to Cajamarca," interrupted Carlos. "It was there that the fate of Peru was decided when Francisco Pizarro with a hundred and eighty undisciplined soldiers, a few muskets, and two ridiculously small cannon defeated the thirty-five thousand warriors of the Inca sovereign Atahualpa."

"Two thousand to one Spaniard," calculated the mestizo with a proud gleam in his eye.

Aimé, poking his fork into a piece of meat, asked, "And how did Pizarro manage to bring off this miracle?"

"He invited the Inca, whom he called 'his brother,' for a visit into his camp," reported Carlos. "All unsuspecting, the Inca arrived with a retinue of many thousands. And in deference to the laws of hospitality, which were sacred to the Peruvians, they came unarmed. Pizarro ambushed them, had the horrified warriors butchered on the spot, and took the Inca prisoner.

"From that moment the entire life of the great realm was paralyzed, for everything had always been done on the personal instructions of the Inca. Atahualpa made a pact with Pizarro: in return for his freedom he would fill a room twenty-two feet long by sixteen feet wide to a height of six and a half feet with gold. Pizarro gave his pledge and the Inca ful-

146

filled his side of the bargain. Treasures worth millions were brought, and Pizarro grabbed the lot. Then he had the Inca killed."

"Nothing remains of all that immense wealth, and only a very little of the once magnificent civilization of these unfortunate people has survived," added Alexander sadly.

The Incas

THEY rode away in silence.

After a few days they reached Loja, with its red-hued forests of cinchona trees. From there, amid hail and snowstorms, they crossed the bleak, uninhabited plateau and then followed southward the broad Inca road at which Hernando Pizarro, Francisco's brother, had exclaimed in wonder, "There is no such road in the whole of Christendom!"

This great road of the Incas had led for nearly a thousand miles high over the Andes and, according to Alexander's calculations, had at some points reached to a height of well over twelve thousand feet. But most of it had been wantonly destroyed after the collapse of the Inca realm.

More than once Alexander shook his fist angrily when he looked up at the remains of the raised stone road running straight as a dart along the rocks. On it one could with ease and safety have reached the valley of the upper Marañón and so the Amazon.

But the road, once paved and flanked by resthouses, now lay in ruins. No government since Inca times had taken the trouble to repair it.

As the mule train could not use the old road, they had to

148

forge their own way through the precipitous canyon of the Rio Guancabamba. Twenty-seven times men and beasts had to ford the broad torrents of the mountain stream, and each time the mules ran the danger of being swept away by the tumultuous current, together with their packs which contained all the specimens and plants collected by Aimé and Alexander during their year of exploration in the Andes. At every crossing the two friends trembled for the life of each one of the heavily laden animals as it struggled to find a safe foothold in the foaming whirlpools.

Farther south they ran into the most unusual postman in the middle of the Rio Guancabamba. It took him two days to make his round, which stretched to the upper reaches of the Amazon, and since the quickest route to the scattered farmsteads was along the rivers he swam the whole way. The young Indian carried the few letters he had to deliver in a cotton cloth wound around his head like a turban.

Every day, as the mule train drew nearer the low-lying

149

lands of the Amazon basin, it grew hotter and Alexander reveled in it. It could never be too hot for him; he hated the cold even though he put up with it when he had to.

Aimé collected a mass of new plants, which compensated him for his meager finds in the mountainous regions. He found twenty-foot-high bougainvillaeas whose brightly colored bracts sheltering insignificant flowers shrouded the plant in a mantle of rose-pink. In the zygophyllum, or bean-caper bush, he recognized a weather prophet, for its delicate pinnate leaves would close before a rainfall.

They stayed for seventeen days in the peaceful valley of the upper Marañón, sleeping under the open sky on the sand of the riverbank as they had done on the Orinoco. Then they made ready to cross the Andes once more, for the fifth time, to visit Cajamarca.

On the way they marveled at the huge, fossilized shells, dating back to prehistoric times, which they found embedded in the limestone on the high mountain passes. Herds of llamas

followed them to the silver mountain of Gualgayoc. Riddled with countless shafts and passages, it rose like an enchanted castle out of the high plateau, and the blue sky showed through its many holes as through a sieve.

The tiny mountain town of Micuipampa, where they made a halt, lay just south of the equator and yet it was so cold there that the water froze at night. Not only the silver mountain but the whole plateau was amazingly rich in precious minerals. Immediately below the grassy turf and entangled with roots lay any amount of red silver ore and fine threads of sterling silver. At one spot boys had found a lump of gold as big as a human head, covered in a web of silver threads.

A narrow gorge, difficult to negotiate even for the mules, led them in six hours from the rugged mountain plateau down into the fertile valley of Cajamarca. They entered the ancient city along an avenue of willows between white, yellow, and red flowering nightshade, gay gardens, and cornfields. Indians in their colorful costumes, bright straw hats on their jet-black hair, came walking toward them. These were the descendants of what had once been the richest nation on earth and to whom gold—the tears of the sun—had proved a terrible curse.

Nothing remained of the palace in which the Inca Atahualpa had reigned, nor of the long stone halls that had once framed the triangular town center, nor of the sun temple and the houses of the sacred sun virgins, and the many other royal buildings of Inca times. Only a few walls on which the Spaniards had erected their own buildings told of the golden days of the Inca rulers.

"We shall have to find somebody who can show us the historic places," said Alexander as they rode into the court-yard of an inn.

"You shall have the best guide in Cajamarca, a direct de-

151

scendant of the last Inca himself," replied Carlos as he led Aimé and Alexander along a street that went to the hot sulfur springs of the Baths of the Incas. They came to a wretchedly poor house, where the clay tiles on the roof, padded with straw, were cracked and dilapidated; a slatted blind obscured the solitary window. It was a one-story building like all the other houses in the town, and the whitewash on the walls, which usually brightens up even the most modest little houses in Spanish colonial towns, had peeled off long ago.

Carlos pushed the door open and stepped into the semidarkness of the interior, followed by Alexander and Aimé.

"Whom do the *señores* seek?" asked a man's voice.

"The Cacique Astorpilca," replied Carlos.

"I am he." Two dark, slightly slanting eyes over a bold nose scrutinized the intruders.

Carlos gave their names. "We have come to greet the last descendant of the great Inca," said Alexander.

Not a muscle moved in Astorpilca's face. "I am sorry I cannot offer the *señores* hospitality. We are poor."

"We have brought wine to drink," said Carlos, taking a round-bellied flask out of his haversack.

At this Astorpilca smiled and raised his hand. "But we have no cut glasses, only calabash tumblers, and no chairs for the *señores* to sit on."

"Why all this ceremony?" said Alexander, laughing. "We are used to sitting on the ground."

"Then you are welcome."

The Peruvian led them onto the patio, a courtyard surrounded by walls covered with jasmine and sweet-scented flowering climbers. Clear water splashed in a fountain, and the steeply slanting roof, supported by pillars, formed a shaded porch.

A woman brought three tumblers and put them on a stool.

152

She wore the old *acsu* dress of Inca times, an ankle-length garment draped sideways about the body and secured with two clasps at the shoulders. A simple leather belt was her only ornament.

"Call the young one," the Peruvian said to her. She nodded and disappeared soundlessly into the house. Turning to Alexander, Astorpilca added, "You will be able to converse better with my son."

While Carlos filled the tumblers, a lad of seventeen stepped through the doorway. He greeted the guests and, looking at him, Alexander thought, So this is what the Inca princes looked like. Had the Spaniards not come to their land, this young man might now rule a kingdom the size of half a continent. He would wear the red tasseled headband of the Inca, the *llautu,* adorned with plumes from the sacred corequenque bird, and he would eat from golden plates and dishes. We, on the other hand, would have to walk barefoot in his presence and carry a load on our backs to show that we were inferior to him.

Now, however, it was the lad who was barefoot, and instead of a regal cape made of the finest vicuña wool and the soft skins of bats he wore a peasant's poncho and a shabby pair of trousers underneath.

"Would you have time to show me Cajamarca and the Baths of the Incas?" Alexander asked him.

The young lad looked at him silently for a moment. "You are not a Spaniard," he said in a low voice.

"No."

"Then I will go with you." After a searching glance at Carlos and a cursory one at Aimé, the young Peruvian turned his eyes back to Alexander and added, "But only with you alone."

"That suits us fine," said Carlos, laughing. "There are only

153

three tumblers and we'll finish the wine without you two."

Alexander and the lad walked on the road that had once been a military highway toward the hot baths of Pultamarca. Even from afar they could see a glow in the air from the rising heat of the sulfur springs. Surrounding them were bare, precipitous rocks of chalk and sandstone.

"Great forests grew here once, and the road we are on was lined with fruit trees. You needed no hat to walk in the shade. My father told me, and he was told by his father."

"That was in the time of the Inca Atahualpa?"

The lad nodded. "It's a long time ago."

"But not so long ago as to be forgotten?"

"No, we don't forget, even though we cannot write," replied the young man earnestly. "Each generation tells the next, as I will tell my son."

"I have been told that you are descended from the last Inca. Is that true?" asked Alexander.

"Yes, I am descended from Atahualpa, to whose baths we are now going," confirmed the lad. He smiled and spoke without a trace of bitterness or reproach in his voice. He accepted his fate with the Indian's calm serenity.

"Atahualpa had a son and a daughter. The son died young, but the daughter, who was christened Angelina by the Spaniards, had a son by Francisco Pizarro. This boy survived everybody—his grandfather Atahualpa, murdered by Pizarro's hangman, his father, who was himself murdered eight years later by his Spanish compatriots, and his uncles, the Inca's brothers, who had no sons."

Little remained of the Inca's summer palace near the sulfur springs. When Alexander inserted his thermometer into the gushing geyser, the mercury soared to 130° F.

Young Astorpilca then led Alexander to a large deep pool where the Inca had taken his baths. "One of the Inca's golden chairs is said to lie down there," he whispered. "White men have searched for it again and again, but no one has ever found it."

"Perhaps the water is too hot," replied Alexander and laughed.

The lad looked puzzled and then asked in an astonished tone, "You are not going to try to find it?"

"I am not interested in gold," said Alexander.

"But you are looking for something, otherwise you would not have come here."

"Certainly—I am interested in plants and rocks, in animals and people. I measure how high the mountains are, how swift the current is in the rivers, the distances between towns. . . ."

The lad shook his head uncomprehendingly, and Alexander tried to explain his meaning more clearly. "In a way I am also a conquistador, but I am a peaceful conqueror who hopes to make life easier for people and help them to a better understanding of nature and of each other."

"All the white men I have met before only wanted gold," answered the lad; "but they will never find the golden chair."

"Why not?"

Astorpilca's son looked around to make sure that no one could hear him. "I'll take you to a place where great treasures are hidden. This secret place is known only to the descendants of the Inca. You won't betray our secret, will you?"

Alexander felt skeptical about this revelation. "I won't betray it, but where is this hiding place?"

"In the mountains behind the palace. But first we must get back to the town."

Leaving the steaming springs, they turned to a sloping field surrounded by crumbling walls. It was here that Atahualpa had received Pizarro's emissaries in the midst of his mighty army, and here he had generously consented to visit the Spanish nobleman next day in the deserted town of Cajamarca. This decision sealed his own fate and brought about the end of a great and unique civilization.

Back in Cajamarca, the young man took Alexander first to the municipal building, the *casa del cabildo,* where his father had his modest office. The Spaniards had given Astorpilca the honorary position of *cacique,* or chief, and it was his duty to settle the minor disputes among his fellow Indians and to deal with their day-to-day affairs.

The building dated back to Inca times; its walls were formed by square-hewn stones, three feet high, which without the aid of cement or mortar fitted so tightly one on top of the other that Alexander could not slide the blade of his knife between them.

Then his guide led him silently into the room where Atahualpa had been kept prisoner for nine months. The lad pointed to the wall where the luckless ruler had made his mark to indicate to what height he would have the room filled with gold bars and gold dishes in return for his freedom. In his mind's eye Alexander could see the treasure pile up, layer upon layer, till it reached well above his head—a breathtaking spectacle. Then he turned away quickly and went out.

"Now we must go to the prison," said the young man.

Here, too, the old Inca masonry was still intact. When they entered the prison chapel the lad crossed himself and knelt down before the altar. On the floor Alexander noticed a long, very thin stone slab of either porphyry or trachytic rock, Alexander couldn't say which.

"Here is his blood," whispered his guide, pointing to some dark spots on the slab. "On this stone Atahualpa was choked to death. No one will ever be able to wipe away these stains."

Alexander frowned. They looked to him more like a horn-

156

blende concentration in the stone than blood, but the lad continued with his story:

"When the gold had been collected from every corner of the Inca's realm, Atahualpa told Pizarro that now he must be allowed to go free. But Pizarro feared that the Inca would take his revenge if he were given his freedom. So he rigged a trial and had his prisoner condemned to death at the stake. However, Atahualpa did not want to be burned, because he had told his people that the sun god would raise him from the dead and send him back to them, and this could not come true if his body were burned to ashes.

"Therefore, when the Spaniards promised him that if he became a Christian he would not have to die by fire, he agreed to be baptized, and since it was St. John's Day he was christened John of Atahualpa. Before his death he was taken outside in his chains and shown a large green comet in the sky to the north. 'This same sign,' said Atahualpa solemnly, 'was seen before my father's death.'

"Then he was taken to his place of execution. All the people of his realm lay prostrate on the earth and wailed. The hangman slung a rope around Atahualpa's neck and throttled him. As he died, drops of blood fell from his mouth onto the stone. This is how Atahualpa, the last Inca of Peru, came to his death."

After these words, the lad crossed himself again and they left the chapel. Outside, the bright sunlight blinded them at first, but they did not have far to go before young Astorpilca stopped by an open shaft that sank deep down into solid rock.

"Down there are subterranean chambers that were excavated in the Inca's lifetime," he whispered mysteriously. "A secret passage leads all the way from here to that stone mound," he added, pointing to a round cupola which rose gently out of the plain. "The chambers and passages have crumbled and fallen in but underneath the mound there are others. . . ." The lad seemed anxious to move on, but Alexander bent down to examine the rock.

It was porphyry, as he had suspected. To sink a shaft into such a hard rock must have been an enormous task.

The more Alexander learned about the engineering feats of the Inca civilization, the more impressed he became. How was it possible for these engineers who had no iron, no carts and horses, to build as they did?

They built roads that would have put the Romans to shame, they developed irrigation systems and laid out tiers of terraces on hillsides. Their fortresses were gigantic and their temples magnificent. Besides, they had a calendar based on very exact astronomical observations, they took regular censuses of the population, and they even had a social service for old people. They knew how to produce bronze which, so Alexander calculated, contained 94 per cent copper and 6 per cent zinc and was almost as hard as steel. Their woven tex-

tiles were the best in the world and their gold work unique.

Thoughtfully Alexander looked at the young lad by his side. Was this great civilization really gone forever, or would it one day rise again and flourish with a new vigor to equal the fame of past glories?

Young Astorpilca now led Alexander crisscross over ground heaped with rubble and stones. He seemed to be looking for something and kept his eyes on the ground. Suddenly he stopped and his eyes shone.

"Here," he said, lowering his voice while his outstretched hand sketched a semicircle in a ceremonial gesture like an incantation. "Here below our feet lies the secret of the Inca. There are paths leading deep down."

"How do you know this?"

The lad took a deep breath as if he had to overcome an inner obstacle before speaking. Had he sensed Alexander's silent thoughts of a moment ago and was he now going to give

159

an answer to the question Alexander had asked himself?

"My great-grandfather," he began, "once took his wife to this place. He bandaged her eyes and led her down below along a maze of passages. But my great-grandfather knew the right way. At last he said to her, 'Take the bandage off but don't be frightened by what you see.' She did as he said and stared about her as in a trance. They were in Atahualpa's golden garden.

"Trees of purest gold stood before her, adorned with shimmering leaves, wonderfully wrought blossoms and sparkling fruits. On the golden branches perched golden birds whose eyes were of jewels. Beautiful gold and silver flowers grew on the ground, and butterflies and insects floated in the air on transparent wings of glittering gems, while lizards, their scales of gold, wriggled between the golden blades of the grass.

"And down there, a little to the left from where you are standing, deep inside the mountain, a broad datura tree with golden blossoms and silver foliage spreads its branches over the Inca's golden chair, which the white men have sought for so long in vain.

" 'Don't touch anything,' my great-grandfather said to his wife. 'All this will stay hidden here until the old times return and the Inca sits again on his sun throne as my father Atahualpa has prophesied. Anyone who takes from this treasure before the appointed time will die the same night!'

"When they had seen everything, my great-grandfather put the bandage back over his wife's eyes and they returned to the surface. She had to swear that she would never speak of what she had seen to the end of her life.

"Each male descendant of the Inca speaks of this secret only once and that is when he tells it to his first-born son. So the knowledge passes from generation to generation. But I could

160

tell you because you are not a Spaniard and you will never return to our land."

When the young Indian fell silent, Alexander raised his head and his glance fell on a cantua flower, the famed "flower of the Inca." Was it mere chance that it happened to grow on this spot?

"The old Spanish historians," said Alexander, "give various reports of the Inca's golden garden. The most beautiful is said to have been in Cuzco, the capital, in the courtyard of the sun temple."

The lad nodded eagerly. "Yes, in the golden hall of this temple, when it was still standing, sat the mummies of the dead Inca kings on their golden chairs ranged along the walls, and above them, high up on the east wall, shone the gigantic sun emblem wrought in the image of the god. It was made of purest gold, and encircling the rays was a setting of brilliant gems, clear as water and sparkling like fire. The chief priest of the sun god saved the emblem from the Spaniards. They searched for it everywhere; they dug up the courtyard and they laid waste whole villages and towns in their search, but they found nothing. It lies hidden deep in the interior of a mountain behind the ice walls of glaciers that never melt, and sheltered by impenetrable forests. No path leads to it and no bridges span the deep canyons that protect it. So the mountain stands guard over the sacred sun, which will one day rise again. Only the condor in its lonely flight high above the clouds knows of the hiding place, and the condor does not speak."

"Let's go back," Alexander interrupted. "My friends will be waiting." They left the stony hillside basking in the blazing heat.

"You and your parents—don't you sometimes feel you would like to dig up these buried treasures?" asked Alexander. "You are poor—very poor, even—and since you are so sure

161

that this golden garden really exists, wouldn't a few branches from it bring you more wealth than all the mines in the Gualgayoc silver mountain?"

The lad shook his head indignantly. "Oh, no," he said proudly. "My father says it would be a crime. If we had those golden branches the white man would start to persecute us all over again. We own a small field and grow good corn in it. That is enough."

They had reached the main plaza of Cajamarca, where the white façade of a great church gleamed in the sun.

When Alexander did not continue the conversation, his guide asked anxiously, "Don't you believe my story?"

"No," was Alexander's curt reply.

"But a little while ago you yourself spoke of the old Spanish historians," recalled young Astorpilca. "Don't you remember what Cieza de León wrote? He came to Peru soon after Atahualpa's death, and he traveled all over the country and saw everything with his own eyes. The Prior of the Franciscan monastery read a passage from his book to me."

"Which one do you mean?"

The lad thought for a minute and then quoted from memory, "All the gold the Spaniards pillaged is but a single drop from a glass of water, compared with the immense treasure the Peruvians managed to hide at the bottom of lakes, rivers, and swamps, or in their mountains."

"León must have exaggerated," said Alexander.

"Well, if you won't believe me, or the Spaniard who was here at the time, I wish the Inca himself could tell you," replied the lad, as much as to say he had done his best and no longer cared whether Alexander believed him or not.

Hardly had he finished speaking when Aimé and Carlos hailed them from the other side of the plaza by the church. The lad gave Alexander a quick, shy look, his dark eyes en-

162

joining him to silence, and Alexander returned the look in mute promise.

"Well, have you made great discoveries?" asked Aimé.

"In these miserable ruins even an Inca couldn't find a piaster," laughed Carlos.

"Why didn't you wait at the *cacique's* house for me?" Alexander wanted to know.

"Because he advised us to look for fresh mules for the next lap of our journey," answered Aimé. "Mules are difficult to come by in Cajamarca."

"The Indians who came with us from the upper Amazon won't go any farther," explained Carlos, turning to young Astorpilca.

"Where are you making for?" the lad asked Alexander.

"For Lima, on the coast to the south."

"I'll see if I can help you," said young Astorpilca, and bowing gracefully he walked away.

"One can tell he is a descendant of the Inca," remarked Aimé, following the departing figure with an admiring glance.

"He is a dreamer," commented Alexander as they walked on.

"That sounds pretty critical, the way you say it."

"No, the lad has made a great impression on me, but he lives in a world of fantasy."

Aimé stopped in his tracks. "A dreamer who lives in a world of fantasy, eh? It seems you have forgotten what you yourself were in your youth."

"I aimed at something, Aimé. I wasn't content merely to dream."

"It took a long time for your dreams to become reality, remember? Who is to say that this young Indian's dreams can't come true one day?"

Honorary Citizen of Mexico

THE long waves of the deep-green Pacific Ocean came rolling in over the rocky shore. Auks, cormorants, and pelicans crowded the beach near the water-line.

Aimé put his hand into the water but withdrew it again quickly. "Why, it's cold!" he said, surprised. "As far as I can remember we are no more than ten degrees south of the equator. I had always thought the Pacific was a warm ocean."

"It is warm," replied Alexander, "but not close to the shore. On the sea-bed a broad current of cold water flows northward along the coast from the icecap of the South Pole."

"No wonder it's cold then."

"Every midshipman who's sailed around Cape Horn knows of this cold stream, which pushes up like a wedge between the warm waters of the Pacific and the South American coast. In its wake sea lions, penguins, and walruses travel from the ice floes of the Antarctic to these lonely beaches where they can find much more food than in the south."

Alexander and Aimé walked along the precipitous cliffs and watched huge formations of cormorants and pelicans flying out to sea like stormclouds in the sky, while gulls dived down into the billowing waves for their prey.

164

These birds nested in millions on the white chalk cliffs, where their droppings had piled up layer upon layer over the centuries.

"Every hundred years these layers of bird dung grow two and a half feet higher," said Alexander. "Even in Inca times it was known that guano, as the deposits are called, makes an excellent manure, and the Indians scattered it on their fields. The Inca even passed a law to protect these birds which performed such a valuable service to agriculture during their breeding season, but today no one bothers about laws of that sort."

Alexander broke off a piece of the gray, crumbly stuff. "I am going to send a sample of this to Paris," he said. "I can't see why the farmers in Europe shouldn't manure their fields with guano just as the Peruvians have done since time immemorial." Hitherto the outside world had taken no interest in this manure, and it was not known that as early as the time of the birth of Christ the peasants of the Peruvian coast had used guano to fertilize their fields.

Alexander was particularly anxious to solve the mystery of the cold water current. He drew up tables of sea temperatures and measured the speed of the current. "You know what an important effect the Gulf Stream has on the climate of western Europe," he said to Aimé. "Starting in the Gulf of Mexico, it crosses the Atlantic Ocean and brings mild winters and ample rainfall in spring and summer to the European coastline. But what effect has this Peruvian current on the climate of western South America?"

The more he thought about it the more convinced he became that this cold stream determined the climate of the narrow strip of lowland between the coast and the Andes. In winter the cold mists rising from the sea brought drizzle and dense fog to the cities, so that between June and September the sun was rarely to be seen in Lima.

At night, while Lima slept, Alexander pursued his astronomical researches. He watched the moon and took lunar measurements to fix the exact geographical position of the Peruvian capital.

Lima had been founded by Francisco Pizarro, and Alexander had a look at the foundation charter in the town hall. Pizarro himself had had no time in his eventful life to learn to read and write, an art of which in any case he thought precious little, and so he had made only two squiggles at the bottom of the charter. Later his private secretary had written his master's name neatly in between. The exact geographical location of the town had not worried Pizarro, and it was left to Alexander to establish it 267 years after the date of its foundation.

"On the ninth of November Mercury will pass in front of

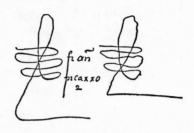

the sun," Alexander told Aimé. "Keep your fingers crossed for a fine day. Mercury is the smallest of the planets, and if it is clearly visible against the sun I shall be able to check my previous calculations based on the revolutions of the moon and on computations by the clock. Then there should be no room for any possible error."

Alexander and Aimé, armed with all their astronomical instruments, watched from a high cliff in the harbor as the tiny planet appeared before the sun. Mercury confirmed Alexander's lunar reckonings, and the exact geographical position of Lima was established once for all.

As Christmas drew near Alexander's thought turned more and more to his return home, and during the holiday he discussed their future plans with Aimé and Carlos. The Regent of Peru had put his own private corvette at their disposal, and while it was not possible to refuse so generous an offer they could hardly monopolize the royal vessel for very long.

"We'll sail north to Guayaquil in it," decided Alexander. "There, close to Chimborazo and Cotopaxi, we can have a look at the coastal district which we did not get to know when we climbed the mountains. . . ."

"And from there it's only a hop to Mexico!" exclaimed Aimé, with the point of his sharpened pencil on the map.

"Let's see," said Alexander.

167

"There, straight as a dart across the ocean to Acapulco," continued Aimé with enthusiasm. "In Mexico you have another great mountain, Popocatepetl, which you can climb, and the most beautiful collection of Aztec ruins which will tell you much more than the meager remains of Inca days."

"While you collect another few thousand new plants! All right—we'll make for Mexico."

Three ancient forts guarded the harbor entrance to Guayaquil. From here the Spaniards had set out on their conquest of Peru, and it was one of the first Spanish towns on the west coast.

Alexander and Aimé, accompanied by Carlos, made one

expedition into the interior of the coastal district from Guayaquil and explored the jungle wilderness near Babahoyo, but they did not have much time to hunt for specimens for their collection. The frigate that was to take them on to Mexico lay ready in the harbor.

On their last evening they walked along the high street of Guayaquil, which runs for a whole mile by the bank of the river Guayas, and looked at the colorful piles of tropical fruit in the shops. Aimé was cautiously biting into an alligator apple, a pulpy fruit whose sweet white flesh smelled of peach blossoms, when Alexander grabbed his arm.

A heavy roll of thunder growled in the distance. The people ran together in the street and looked up toward the mountains on the horizon where the sky had begun to turn blood red.

"It's Cotopaxi!" someone cried out.

From the summit of Cotopaxi, the highest active volcano on earth, an immense pillar of fire shot up toward the stars. The mantle of snow that lay wrapped around its shoulders like an ermine cloak began to melt visibly, and the black contours of the mountain stood out stark and naked against the night sky illuminated by the bright flashes of fire.

In May of the previous year Alexander and Aimé had climbed close to its summit, and now, as they were about to leave South America, it bade them farewell with a nonstop salute of thunder and belching flames.

All night long they listened to the ominous roar in the distance. Suddenly Aimé asked, "Do you remember that strangely shaped rock that we saw near the summit? Its pointed crags jutted out like the features of a face. The people in the valley call it 'the head of the Inca.' "

"How do you know that?"

"An old man told me that this rock appeared during a

169

tremendous eruption at the exact hour when Atahualpa was strangled in Cajamarca."

"To believe that you'd have to suppose that Cotopaxi had never erupted before," said Alexander dryly. He thought for a while and then continued, "It's true, though, that an eruption is said to have occurred at the time of the conquest of Peru and that the rain of hot ash had frightened the Spaniards."

"If only you were just a little superstitious, you might imagine that the Inca on the volcano was calling you."

"Why me especially?"

"Isn't it strange that the mountain should start to thunder and spit fire just when we are leaving?" speculated Aimé.

"You've got a wonderful imagination," commented Alexander, but Aimé was not to be put off as easily as that.

"Perhaps he wanted to remind you of something."

"Of what?"

"I don't know what young Astorpilca told you in Cajamarca, but he was a direct descendant of the Inca, wasn't he? Perhaps Atahualpa wants to convince you that whatever his great-grandson believes may one day come about."

While the mountain growled and thundered, Alexander remembered how the lad had wished the Inca himself could speak to him, since Alexander would not believe what he had been told.

Next morning, when the frigate hoisted her sails, Cotopaxi's distant growl could still be heard from far out to sea. Dark clouds draped the sun like black mourning crape.

During the voyage Alexander wrote a letter to the Viceroy of Mexico, asking for permission to explore his country, and as soon as they had arrived in Acapulco he posted it. After only a few days a royal messenger brought a most gracious reply from the Viceroy offering Alexander and his friends all the assistance they might need. The necessary passports and documents for their journey were enclosed.

"This ruler doesn't know me, he has never even seen me, and yet he offers to help me in every way because I am a scientist. In return, I shall make him a present that will be worthy of his trust and hospitality," said Alexander.

"A present?" wondered Aimé, fearing that he might be asked to sacrifice a part of his precious butterfly collection, but he was on the wrong track.

"No one has ever written a detailed account of Mexico," Alexander continued. "There is no one book that describes its history and civilization and also tells of its climate and scenery, its people and their way of life. I shall write a book to tell the world all about Mexico."

Aimé and Carlos looked at him dubiously. They knew his immense capacity for work, but such a book would, they thought, require a whole group of researchers.

"I'm afraid this may be too big an undertaking," ventured Aimé thoughtfully.

"We shall see," replied Alexander. "First we will go to the capital and from there we'll explore the whole country in all directions."

And so it was. Early in April, 1803, they set out from Acapulco for Mexico City prepared to collect information of every sort along the way. Alexander was as much interested in the incidence of smallpox, which killed many Mexicans, as in how heavy a load of silver ore a miner had to carry on his back. He counted the banana plants that grew in an area of a hundred square miles, and he looked into the cooking pots of the Indian women, noting down what the country people ate and drank. With the help of Aimé and Carlos, he built a raft of gourd shells tied together with agave fibers, and on

this the three of them tossed about on a mountain stream to give Alexander first-hand experience of a mode of travel commonly used by the Mexican Indians.

After a fortnight they arrived in Mexico City. All the buildings there seemed to be of more than normal size. The cathedral in the main square was the biggest church on the American continent, the Viceroy's palace had a frontage of more than two hundred yards, and Alexander was particularly impressed by the magnificent institute for mining engineers which was being built at the time of his visit.

Aimé, on his part, was amazed by the abundance of blossom everywhere. Every stall in the countless little markets was decorated with fresh flowers. The young Indian girls wore flowers in their hair as, with a regal gait, they walked barefoot about the streets in their colorful costumes.

On their first evening both friends agreed that Mexico City was the most beautiful town in the world.

172

Above the town rose Chapultepec—Grasshopper Hill —where the Aztecs used to bury their kings. Now a castle stood on its rocky top, and Alexander thought that from there they would get a good view of the surrounding countryside and the Mexican uplands. So next morning the three of them climbed Chapultepec.

The tops of ancient cypresses towered above groves of locusts and bananas, pepper shrubs and palms. A magnificent view spread out before them, and Alexander described it in his notebook.

"This porphyry rock overlooks an immense plain and vast stretches of cultivated land which extend right to the high mountain chain covered in eternal snow.

"To the north, nestling against the mountains, between ravines overgrown with date palms and tree-high palm lilies, the palatial convent of Our Lady of Guadalupe can be seen.

"To the south the country is one gigantic orchard of peach, apple, and cherry trees.

"All this fertile land stands in vivid contrast to the rugged mountain chain that encloses the valley, above which tower the volcanoes Popocatepetl and Iztaccihuatl. Flames rise continuously from the crater of Popocatepetl as it belches smoke and ashes over its cloak of ice and snow."

While Alexander was writing, a Mexican had come up to greet them. "May we have a look at the castle?" Carlos asked him.

The Mexican laughed. "You may buy it, *Señor*. The government is anxious to get rid of it."

Aimé thought he might as well ask the price, but the Mexican assured him that he needn't buy the whole castle; he could have just one window frame or a door.

However, Aimé would not be tempted. It might have been different if he had been offered one of the floating gardens of Xochimilco, where the flowers grew that every Mexican girl wore in her hair.

These gardens had been laid out by the Aztecs when the city still stood on stilts in the middle of a large group of lakes, rather like Venice. The Spaniards replaced the old water town, which was often flooded, by a new town on dry ground. They tore down all the old buildings and drained the lakes or filled them in. The gardens of Xochimilco, interlaced by narrow canals, were the sole reminder of an ancient splendor when the white temples and palaces of a dream town rose amid green palms from the deep-blue waters of the lakes.

The gardens literally floated on the water. The Indians made rafts of reeds, branches, and roots, covered them with black earth, and on them they grew peas, red peppers, and

174

other vegetables. Around the edge of the raft ran a border of flowers, sometimes even a rose hedge.

When Alexander and the others returned to their hotel in the evening, a palace official was waiting for him with an invitation from the Viceroy. After a splendid dinner at which the best Spanish wines were served, the Viceroy took his guest into the garden, where Alexander laid before him his plans about the book on Mexico.

"Will you be writing about the Aztecs too?" wondered the Viceroy.

"I mean to, Sire," replied Alexander.

"Then you must come to my library with me. I have a few manuscripts from Aztec times that will interest you."

Carefully the Viceroy spread the books before Alexander. They were bound in tablets of light wood between which the pages lay tightly folded like a concertina. Alexander opened one and drew it apart. It was almost six feet long, and told in colorful pictures of the migration of the Aztecs from the Rio Gila to the plateau of Mexico City, of the foundation of the Aztec towns and their wars with neighboring peoples.

"Unfortunately, not many of these painted picture books have come down to us, although Montezuma, the last Aztec ruler, employed thousands of artists and scribes," said the Viceroy. "The Aztecs wrote and painted on paper made of agave leaves, on cured deerskins, and on cotton. I am sure these books will tell you a lot about their culture and way of life."

After his meeting with the Viceroy Alexander had free access to the royal library. He translated the Aztecs' picture script and pondered on their origin, their history and ancient customs. He also read eyewitness accounts by Spaniards who had fought by the side of the conqueror Cortez, and told of the fall and total destruction of this once great civilization.

175

One day the friends rode out to the pyramids of Teotihua-cán, which, so the legend goes, were erected on the spot whence the sun and moon began their course in the heavens.

Sacred shrines and temples had stood on the uppermost tiers of these pyramids, and there a host of Aztec priests had performed cruel, bloodthirsty rites. They worshiped the sun and feared that one day it would disappear from the sky and the world would end.

According to their belief, there had already been four suns and four world eras before their own time. These were the water sun, extinguished by the flood when all men were turned into fish; the jaguar sun, shattered by a collapse of the sky, after which the jaguars devoured all the people; the rain-of-fire sun, burned out when it rained fire and the people died in the flames; and the wind sun, which disappeared after a terrible hurricane when all human beings were turned into apes.

The sun of their own day had been created by the storm god Quetzalcoatl, and the Aztec priests called it the earth-quake sun. Their sacred picture scriptures prophesied that this sun would go down together with the world in a great earth-quake.

Even today the uplands of Mexico are frequently shaken by severe quakes which often cause devastation in the vicinity of the capital. No wonder that the Aztecs lived in constant fear at the slightest tremor, since it might herald the end of their world.

To keep the sun in the sky and ensure that it would never grow old and weak, it had to be offered nourishing food and sacrifices great enough to renew its strength. And what sacrifice could be greater than that of a human being?

So the Aztec priests offered up human beings. They laid the victims on the altar, cut them open with stone knives,

176

and wrenched the beating hearts from their living bodies. The hearts were then offered to the sun on a sacred salver.

The blood of the victims was considered sacred too, and the priests believed that they would profane the sacrifice if they washed off the blood that splashed all over them during the gruesome ceremony. When the Spaniards came they were horrified at their first sight of an Aztec priest encrusted from head to foot in dried blood.

To dull their constant fear of the end of the world, the Aztecs offered up more and more human sacrifices. At the consecration of one new temple they sacrificed no fewer than twenty thousand prisoners, and at another shrine the Spaniards discovered immense numbers of human skulls neatly piled on racks.

Alexander did not concentrate solely on these grisly reminders of the past; he was just as much interested in the Mexico of his own time. On his travels all over the kingdom he visited more than seventy towns and districts and learned to distinguish between twenty or so languages spoken by the various tribes and races.

Aimé preferred to sample the delicious fruits and delicacies offered by the markets and cookshops of the town. He found chunks of avocado pear floating in his soup and ate its soft flesh spread on his bread like butter. He loved the mangoes, with their piquant taste and aroma, and the egg-shaped granadillas. When he had had enough of the sweet fruits of the markets, he went to the steaming caldron of one of the *cabezeros,* portable kitchens that were carried from place to place on a stretcher by two street vendors who advertised their wares with loud cries. Aimé would choose a piece of highly seasoned meat from the caldron filled with large chunks of beef, pork, and mutton simmering in a biting-hot chili sauce.

To wash it down he would drink a glass of *pulque*, a milky-white liquid made of the fermented sap of magueys. All Mexico drank *pulque*. Aimé had long since become used to its peculiar smell, but Alexander maintained that it reeked like foul meat or rancid cheese.

Among other delicacies greatly favored by the Mexicans were fried maggots as long as fingers—the maguey worms—skinned frogs in a rich sauce, and salamanders from Lake Texcoco.

Aimé took two live specimens of these salamanders, called axolotls, to Alexander in a water jug. "You can have them roasted or baked with chili sauce in Indian fashion, or pickled in vinegar as the Spaniards favor them," he said. "They taste like eels."

"Nonsense!" exclaimed Alexander, but he looked at the creatures with interest. "They look like our pond salamanders at home, except that they are bigger and fatter. But they are not fully grown. They are still tadpoles, otherwise they wouldn't have gills."

"I have been told they are never found without gills," explained Aimé.

Alexander thought for a bit. "Perhaps they remain tadpoles all their lives. But how do they reproduce if they never grow up? We'll take a couple of these interesting creatures back to Paris with us," he decided.

Little did he know that this decision would let loose a storm of controversy among zoologists. Were they grown salamanders with gills, or still at the larval stage as tadpoles are? The controversy went on for sixty years, and in the end Alexander was proved right—they were tadpoles. But these obstinate creatures were capable of reproducing themselves at the larval stage, so most of them never bothered to shed their gills and start breathing through the lungs, like grown land salamanders.

Alexander and Aimé remained in Mexico City for a whole year. Then the book was finished. Alexander presented it to the Viceroy, who exclaimed enthusiastically, "This is a truly great book which will outlive all of us. Generations to come will learn from it and Mexico will always be proud of it."

The Viceroy's words have come true. Published in four volumes, Alexander's book, *Political Essay on the Kingdom of New Spain,* has remained a standard work of reference and a model to future writers of how such a study of a whole country should be written. In recognition of his work, Alexander was made an honorary citizen of Mexico.

Aimé had grown restive during their long stay in the city and was happy when they were finally on their way to Veracruz, on the Gulf of Mexico. They passed through the densely populated country of Puebla and made a halt in Cholula.

Here Aimé was amazed by the large number of churches that stood dotted about among groves of trees, yellow cornfields, and green agave plantations. "There are exactly three hundred and sixty-five churches in this town—a church for every day in the year," announced Carlos, who had learned this fact from Alexander's notes.

"Cholula was once the sacred city of the Aztecs," explained Alexander. "There were more temples and priests here than in the capital. Moreover, it can boast of one of the architectural wonders of the New World. It has a gigantic pyramid."

"I can't see any pyramid," said Aimé, looking around.

"It's over there, that green hill on which a church stands. It was once the biggest man-built structure in all America. According to Indian legend it was erected by a giant."

Aimé shook his head. He had to have a closer look at this

wonder of the world. At first he could see nothing but an overgrown hill of clayey soil, but on closer examination he could make out layers of unburned bricks, each of which was almost twenty inches long. Alexander paced along one side of the mountain and announced, "It's almost three hundred yards long. The sides of the pyramid of Cheops in Egypt measure only a little over two hundred yards."

"On the uppermost tier of the pyramid," Alexander told his friends, "where the church is now, in Aztec time there stood the altar of the god Quetzalcoatl. This god was believed to have lived in Cholula for twenty years. He was a white man and wore a beard. He taught the people how to smelt metals and admonished them to keep the peace. In his time only the fruits of the fields were offered as sacrifices to the gods.

"After twenty years Quetzalcoatl took his leave, saying that he would return to the land of his fathers whence he had come, but that they should not be sad. 'Live according to my teaching, for I shall come back one day,' he said, and went away from Cholula to the east across the sea.

"Ever since his departure the Aztecs have been waiting for his return. When Cortez' small army landed in Mexico, their ruler Montezuma mistook the leader of these blond and bearded men, who had come from the east, for the returning god Quetzalcoatl. By messengers he sent him the raiment of the gods of East and West, North and South, whom he was said to personify. We know that Montezuma and all the Aztecs paid dearly for having mistaken Cortez for a god!" concluded Alexander.

After a few days in Cholula, the friends continued their journey to Veracruz, the *Ciudad de los Muertos,* or the "City of the Dead," as the Spaniards called this harbor town sweltering amid an arid, desolate wasteland. Huge sand dunes hugged the walls of the town. The heat was stifling; there

180

wasn't a drop of drinking water, and yellow fever was rampant among the townspeople. From the roofs of the low houses black vultures gaped down curiously at the visitors.

"This town looks quite Oriental," said Carlos, and pointed to the cupolas of the churches from whose colorfully glazed tiles slender turrets like minarets rose into the sky. "Still, I don't want to be buried here," he added, wiping the sweat from his forehead.

"All the same, it might easily happen," was Aimé's comforting rejoinder. "You arrive as an unsuspecting visitor, after three days you go to bed with a fever, on the fifth day you start throwing up black vomit, and then you know that you have yellow fever. If you still feel like looking at yourself, you'll find that your face first turns bright yellow like a lemon and then a deep bronze color."

"Do many people die of it?"

Aimé nodded. "Thirty out of every hundred, sometimes as many as eighty."

Carlos swallowed nervously. "Are we staying long in Veracruz?" he wanted to know. To his relief they soon found a frigate in the harbor to take them across the Gulf to Havana.

Carlos was in charge of the baggage, which required a separate sloop for the voyage. The two axolotls were swimming about happily in their tin water tank on top of the cases containing the herbariums and drawings, mummified heads, crocodile skins, and Aztec manuscripts. In addition there were mineral specimens, tubes filled with curare, and in small linen pouches thousands of seeds of exotic flowers that would one day delight the ladies of Europe with the umdreamed-of splendor of their blooms.

Carlos watched over the axolotls anxiously and fed them regularly.

"Pity that you weren't with us on the Orinoco," remarked

Aimé. "There you would have had a whole menagerie to look after."

"These two ugly salamanders are quite enough headache for me," said Carlos. "I shall be glad when we get them to Paris."

"Paris!" exclaimed Aimé. "You will have to wait a few months for that. So far we have only rubbed shoulders with Kings and Viceroys. Now we are going to shake hands with the democratic President of the United States, Thomas Jefferson, who has just bought Louisiana—a territory five times as big as France—from Napoleon."

And so it was. President Jefferson received Alexander at Monticello with open arms and kept him there for three weeks. He wanted to know all about conditions in Mexico and South America, and Alexander gave him a detailed report. Later the President introduced him to other leading personalities in the young democracy. Alexander had long and animated discussions with men who were ready to learn from anyone who had, like him, wandered about the world with open eyes.

Showered with honors and public recognition, Alexander left the United States after a two-month stay and set sail for Europe in the *Favorite* together with Aimé and Carlos and all their possessions, including the axolotls.

Conclusion

NAPOLEON'S blue eyes measured Alexander coldly. "So," he said, "you busy yourself with botany. My wife does the same." With this he turned on his heels and left Alexander abruptly. Aimé was not honored with so much as a glance.

Alexander looked after the departing Emperor with a thoughtful, almost sad expression. He remembered Atahualpa. There had been the same pomp and majesty at his court, the same proud generals, the same display of might and power. And so it had been at the court of the Aztec ruler Montezuma, also.

Alexander's eyes had seen the rubble and ruins that were all that was left of this ancient glory in the empires beyond the sea. He shuddered at the thought of what fate might lie in store for Europe.

"For this you bought yourself a velvet frock coat," whispered Aimé contemptuously.

"The evening isn't over yet," replied Alexander equally quietly, and at that moment an equerry came up to them and said that he had orders to present Baron von Humboldt and Monsieur Bonpland to Her Majesty the Empress.

Charmingly and graciously, as was her way, the Empress

Josephine thanked Aimé for the plants he had presented to her and which were now flourishing in the glasshouses of her summer place at Malmaison. They reminded her of the island of Martinique, where she was born.

Quick to grasp the opportunity, Alexander began to sing Aimé's praises, pointing out that his flowers from Peru and Mexico now enriched the gardens of Paris while he himself remained poor. The Academy was ready to grant him a pension, but the Emperor's signature had yet to be secured.

Aimé went hot and cold all over while Alexander talked, but the Empress smiled. A few days later an imperial decree granted the botanist Dr. Aimé Bonpland, on the express recommendation of Herr von Humboldt, a yearly pension of three thousand francs. It was only half the amount Alexander had hoped for, but Aimé was satisfied. "If I earn a little extra, I'll manage," he said modestly.

Hard times were to come to both friends, as to the whole of Europe, in the years following their return from South America.

Alexander worked incessantly. He lectured, conducted scientific experiments in laboratories, and expounded his views on astronomy, chemistry, botany, and geography to his fellow scientists. Above all he wrote books. His diaries and journals of the South American expedition filled three large volumes, to which were added two magnificent volumes of illustrations. Then there were separate volumes devoted to descriptions of animals, and others to discussions on astronomy and topography. In the end the mammoth work grew to twenty folio volumes with 1,425 pictures and maps.

But his favorite book, the one he himself liked best, was a more popular work which he called *Views of Nature*. In it he asked his readers to go with him into the dense green jungle, to the wide-open spaces of the savanna, and up to the high mountaintops of the Andes.

The many scientific works, each as big as an atlas, were furnished with costly copperplate engravings, while the four folios of plant illustrations that Aimé prepared contained over 250 hand-painted color plates, a separate one for each plant.

The publication of all these works brought Alexander close to bankruptcy. He was saved from want only by the Berlin Academy, which granted him an annual stipend in recognition of his many achievements.

Meanwhile Aimé had presented his herbarium to the French nation and was waiting impatiently in Paris for the day when he and Alexander could start out on their long-planned expedition to India. But year after year their plans had to be postponed while Napoleon, his coffers swollen by the Louisiana millions, turned all Europe from Spain to Russia into a battlefield.

Empress Josephine, discarded by Napoleon in favor of a young Austrian archduchess, died brokenhearted in Navarre. When her body was taken to Malmaison, Aimé paid his last tribute to her. He had never forgotten his first meeting with her and later, when he sent her his beautiful volumes on the flora of South America, she had made him curator of the imperial gardens at her beloved summer place. With her enthusiastic support, Aimé had turned these gardens into a veritable paradise of rare, exotic flowers and shrubs.

Cometlike, Napoleon's star rose to its zenith and then fell from the sky in a few short years.

While Europe lay in the grip of war and its aftermath, unrest and uprisings against the Spaniards broke out in various parts of South America. Simón Bolívar visited Alexander in Paris and had long discussions with him. "Is South America

185

ready for freedom?" Bolívar asked him, and Alexander answered, "All nations are entitled to their freedom. Without freedom there can be no development."

Encouraged by these words, Simón Bolívar, accompanied by Carlos, returned to South America. He led the revolution in Venezuela and made a triumphal entry into Caracas as its liberator. The three-hundred-year-old rule of the conquistadors was at an end.

"When are we going to India?" Tirelessly Aimé asked this same question, but even now after Napoleon's downfall the East India Company prevaricated and delayed issuing the necessary documents. There were always fresh reasons why the time was not opportune for such an expedition. Finally Aimé's patience was exhausted.

"I have been offered a professorship in Natural History at Buenos Aires," he told Alexander. "Should I accept?"

Alexander immediately advised him to do so. "But stay clear of the countries to the north of Argentina. Simón Bolívar may be the liberator of South America, but he is a long way yet from being victorious."

"Won't you come too?" Aimé urged. "These young nations need men like us."

Alexander frowned thoughtfully. He would have been only too glad to turn his back on Europe, but he felt that as long as there was the slightest chance of an expedition to Asia he should stay.

So the two friends parted. Alexander's last words were, "Don't rely too much on your luck, Aimé—and let us hear from you."

After the first few letters, however, Aimé fell silent, and for ten long years there was no word from him. Dame Fortune had turned against him in the very hour when he had

186

felt most secure and settled. The professorship in Buenos Aires was not a great success, because there was only a handful of students to attend his lectures, and so Aimé had started a plantation up-country on the banks of the Paraná River where Argentina adjoins Paraguay. Everything he grew bore an abundant harvest in the fertile soil, but his most successful crop was tea—yerba maté. This tea is made by pouring boiling water on the pulverized leaves of the yerba plant and is the universal drink throughout most of South America. Aimé had found six wild-growing varieties of the yerba in the jungles of Argentina and was cultivating them on his plantation.

Across the border, the dictator of Paraguay, Rodríguez Francia, considered the cultivation of yerba maté the exclusive monopoly of Paraguay, and one day his soldiers crossed the river, sacked and burned Aimé's plantation, and carted him off in chains to Santa Maria.

Francia, a demented fanatic who saw himself surrounded by imaginary enemies, kept Aimé prisoner for ten years on the pretext that, besides having cultivated yerba maté, he had also enticed the Indian tribes to invade Paraguay.

As soon as Alexander heard the news, he aroused the scientific world to send a special emissary to Asunción to plead with Francia. But to no avail. Alexander sent a personal letter and a set of his great work on South America in an effort to

persuade the dictator to set his friend free. Francia merely tore up the letter and put the books into his library.

Penniless and isolated from the outside world, Aimé bore his fate stoically. He was allowed to move about freely within a radius of a few miles of Santa Maria, and he practiced medicine among the poor Indians who were his only companions.

During all this time Alexander's fame spread throughout Europe. His hopes for an expedition to Asia reached fulfillment—not in India, as he had planned, but in Siberia and China. The Russian government invited him to travel all over their vast country, and so it came about that Alexander celebrated his sixtieth birthday in Siberia. From there he went on to Mongolia and China before returning to St. Petersburg.

By a strange coincidence Aimé regained his freedom at

almost exactly the same time as Alexander set out for Russia. Transported back across the river by Francia's soldiers onto Argentine soil, he was once again a free man, but he was completely destitute for he had had to leave behind even the few miserable possessions he had managed to collect in captivity.

When Alexander returned to Berlin from Russia, where he had been feted and honored by the Tsar and the Tsarina, the two now aging friends met for the last time. Alexander was well aware of Aimé's straitened circumstances, even though his old friend tried to conceal them from him. Using his enormous influence in the chancelleries of Europe, Alexander managed to persuade the French government to pay Aimé the arrears of his pension, which had lapsed during his enforced stay in Paraguay.

Armed with this sum of money, Aimé settled permanently in Argentina, bought a piece of land, and at the age of sixty-nine married an Indian woman with whom he had several children. With never a thought of envy, he rejoiced in Alexander's world-wide reputation, and was happy in the thought that he had helped his great friend in some small measure to reach the pinnacle of an extraordinary career. In a letter to Alexander he wrote:

"I am sure you must draw satisfaction from your success and fame, which increases with every year. You must live until you are a hundred, and then you'll begin a second lifetime which will last forever."

Alexander, by then nearly eighty, replied that he was about to begin the most important literary work of his life: "I have the mad idea to put the whole material world, everything we know today of the firmament and of life on earth, from the Milky Way to the tiniest moss on a rock, into a single work. My title for it will be *Cosmos*."

Unendingly Alexander worked, partly in Potsdam and

190

partly in his apartment in Berlin or in the castle of Charlottenhof, where the Crown Prince had put two rooms at his disposal.

When the first two volumes of *Cosmos* were published, eager buyers stormed the bookshops and staged pitched battles to get possession of copies of the book.

Cosmos was translated into all the principal languages of the world, and became one of the most widely read books of its time, but it was never finished.

On a sunny May day, almost exactly a year to the day after Aimé had closed his eyes forever on his sun-drenched plantation, death came to ninety-year-old Alexander, still tirelessly at work on the fifth volume of *Cosmos*.

He was laid to rest near his old family home by the lake where, as a small and sickly boy of whose future everyone despaired, he had once collected pebbles on the shore.

Mountains and rivers, parks and cities and stones have been named after Alexander von Humboldt. The soft glimmer of Polar lights casts a mysterious glow on the Humboldt glaciers in the north of Greenland. The Humboldt Current sweeps around the coast of South America; and in California, an inlet of the Pacific Ocean is called Humboldt Bay.

Between San Francisco and Chicago trains race along the Humboldt River and at an elevation of nine thousand feet cross the Humboldt Mountains which form the backbone of the huge desert bowl between the Sierra Nevada and the Rocky Mountains. The guacharos, those strange night birds which Alexander described for the first time, nest safely among the dark rocks in the caves of Caripe in Venezuela. The government has placed them under its protection. Their habitat today carries the proud name of Humboldt National Park.

In the Cordillera Mérida in west Venezuela two towering

giants of granite stand close together. At their feet the boiling Chama races past. Permanent glaciers crown their peaks at a height of fifteen thousand feet. Their names are Humboldt and Bonpland.

In centuries to come, after all traces of humanity have been eradicated, these two mountains will still stand side by side, two friends, loyal beyond time and eternity.